FATHERS OF INDUSTRIES

FATHERS OF INDUSTRIES

BY LEONARD M. FANNING

ILLUSTRATED BY ALBERT ORBAAN

J. B. LIPPINCOTT COMPANY

PHILADELPHIA . NEW YORK

CONTENTS

6   CONTENTS

- 1 -

THE WORLD BEFORE MODERN HISTORY

BEFORE THE EARLIEST RECORDS of history man had built great empires. As the story of the ancient world unfolds, those civilizations already had crumbled into ruins and legend, but from their dust new empires arose to fabulous heights.

Mining, metalworking, woodworking, agriculture, spinning and weaving, building, shipbuilding and navigation occupied ancient man, and his creative arts attained a magnificence and splendor never since excelled.

To further his trade, science and art, ancient man had no power except that produced by animals. Oxen, asses, camels, elephants, horses, dogs and human slaves were his principal prime movers.

Man's constant urge was for increased power, to devise new and greater prime movers. His reason was sim-

7

ple. With greater power he could do more work with less effort, less drudgery.

Sailing vessels and water wheels first enlarged man's power. Roman barges—human power plants, each with one to five banks of oars pulled by straining slaves—plied the blue Mediterranean, assisted only slightly by sails.

The ancients also coupled oxen or horses in tandem and harnessed slaves together—the first "central power stations." In the time of Emperor Augustus Caesar (27 B.C.–A.D. 14), Caecilius, a freeman of Rome, operated a 4116-slave unit that we would rate today at 400 horsepower. So except for sail and the water wheel, the muscles of man and beast supplied most of ancient man's power. He had no engines.

Nevertheless, learned experimenters and scholars were striving to lighten man's load. In their laboratories, or sometimes only in their writings, they devised quaint "engines."

In his *Pneumatica,* Hero, Greek mathematician of Alexandria (about 130 B.C.), describes a device which may be called a primitive steam reaction turbine. Hero used steam to whirl the ball—the first recorded experiment with steam power. He named his "engine" an aeolipile after Aeolus, the Greek god of wind.

The ancients' machines were few. Often they were mere toys or preposterous, Rube Goldberg gadgets that brought only ridicule upon the experimenters.

Nevertheless, the scholars progressed somewhat in developing ways to relieve man's backache. They suggested—and sometimes used—principles from which, centuries later, machine inventions materialized.

The Greek philosopher, Aristotle (384–322 B.C.), in his *Mechanical Problems,* mentions the lever, widely applied in drawing water from wells; the wedge, the winch, the roller, the wheel, the pulley and the core wheel—the last a forerunner of the gear.

Archimedes, the Greek mathematician (287–212 B.C.), recommended a "rotary pump" to suck water from the hold of a large ship built by King Hiero II of Syracuse. His screw came into practical use on the Nile to draw water and, later, to squeeze the oil from olives.

Archimedes also described an apparatus, consisting of a windlass, rope and pulley, operated by manpower and, apparently, used for hoisting objects from level to level —the first elevator! In the palace of the Roman Emperor Nero (37–68 A.D.) three lifts, similar to Archimedes' "elevator," were used by the fat monarch.

But centuries passed before the Machine Age arrived to give practical form to the "engines" and "machines" of Hero and other experimenters. Indeed, the mechanical principles of the ancients were somewhat obscure and had limitations which permitted few advances.

By and large, then, ancient man's power was his muscle. In a world of cruelty and bondage, by sweat and whip, slave labor built Egypt, Athens and Rome. The pyramids of Egypt, the Acropolis of Athens, the Coliseum of Rome and the Appian Way—the Romans' great paved highway built in the third and second centuries before Christ—stand today as imperishable monuments to perishable civilizations.

The first vehicles—sledges dragged by domestic or human animals—remained in the ancient world even after the wheel had come into use. Homer, the Greek poet (about 850 B.C.), refers to the existence of chariots as early as 2200 B.C. and describes them as so light that a strong man could carry one in his arms.

Ancient Egypt had no wagons. The Egyptians simply couldn't make them rugged enough for their huge building projects. Once, by sledge, they dragged a stone weighing 887 tons over a hundred miles. Two thousand slaves required three years to complete the job. The builders' ingenuity we recognize. The drudgery and misery of those human beings we prefer to forget.

But we can find much to admire in the first carriage —the sleek, swift chariot of the Egyptians. Beautifully constructed, it heralded a new era of land transportation built upon the wheel. In wheeled vehicles man combined utility with pleasure. Like the Egyptians before them, the Greeks and Romans employed the chariot widely. Though it was without the luxury of springs or seat, ancient man used the chariot in war games, hunting and racing. But the Greeks were the first to develop a practical, workaday, four-wheeled wagon. Inevitably the road-building Roman conquerors influenced the wider use of vehicles.

On the Appian Way in Roman times one would have seen land transportation at an interesting stage of evolution—a Roman governor lolling in his ponderous coach, a peddler riding on a donkey, a cohort of legionnaires marching shackled prisoners to Rome for trial and slavery, a young dandy exhibiting the paces of a fine horse.

One might also have seen slaves carrying on their shoulders a palanquin containing two ladies, caravans of heavy, donkey-driven wagons with groaning axles and government courtiers flashing by in swift, gaudy chariots. Yet Roman transport was quite primitive.

Ancient civilizations grew to magnificent physical as well as cultural dimensions. Within its walls Alexandria enfolded 750,000 persons, Carthage, 1,000,000, and Rome, 1,500,000. But the homes of the people were crude, unlighted shelters. Though Egypt stood at the top of the civilized world, it housed most of its people in mud-plaster hovels. They cooked, ate and spent the major part of their lives out of doors.

Despite its show places—its Acropolis, its theater of Dionysus and its beautiful temples—Athens was a city unbeautiful, if judged by its small, squalid homes. During the Golden Age, in fact, the meanness of the home was counted as a virtue. Both Greeks and Egyptians overcame stenches in their houses with perfume.

Epidemics swept the cities. However, the Greek physician Hippocrates (460–377? B.C.), called the father of medicine, warded off several plagues by adjusting house windows and other openings to secure a constant draft. Of the ancient civilizations Rome alone improved living conditions. Pure drinking water flowed into the city from the mountains in great aqueducts. Rome's baths became an institution. Its stone sewerage systems greatly advanced sanitation. The city suffered no plagues, such as the Black Death, which periodically swept Europe during the later Middle Ages.

Wealthy Romans lived in homes that were practically

hotels and vied with each other in supplying hospitality and entertainment. Nevertheless, as in Egypt and Greece, most Roman people inhabited houses with dark rooms, inefficient hearths, a bench or two for furniture and heaps of straw for beds. Rome built the first tenements, calling them "islands." They towered high above ground-floor shops, and the tenants reached the upper stories by treacherous outside wooden stairs, some with more than two hundred steps. Finally, Emperor Augustus limited the height of tenements to seventy feet. Home, for most people of the ancient world, was hardly a livable place.

Following the fall of a Rome degenerated by laziness and luxury came the Middle Ages, significantly known also as the Dark Ages. Civilization lapsed. People groped in mysticism, superstition, unreality.

For hundreds of years barbaric tribes swarmed over Europe. Scarcely did man use the wheel that he had invented, for if he had to travel he preferred horseback. Even with bodyguards people journeyed fearfully through unlighted, disease-infested streets or over lonely roads where highwaymen and marauders lurked. Virtually continuous warfare existed. Every countryside was an armed camp. Order and government were almost lost. Most people remained at home. The great civilizing force of moving about, of meeting the people of other nations, received an appalling setback.

Man's creative impulse to improve his lot was frustrated. Tumult, fear and isolation were not conducive to research. Not until the fourteenth and fifteenth centuries, fifteen hundred years after Hero and Archimedes, did man advance in either the theory or practice of invention and mechanics!

Though barbarians conquered Rome's armies, eventually Rome's civilization conquered them. Slowly, painstakingly, man erected another civilization by adapting to his own use the best that Rome had to offer. During the fourteenth and fifteenth centuries came the Renaissance—which literally means "revival" or "rebirth"—when man reawakened to the culture and spirit of the ancient world.

But the rebirth was more than a recapturing of things past. It marked the entrance of European nations to a fresh and vital stage upon which freedom of thought and of action—new freedoms both—held sway. The age of western European culture was dawning.

During the Renaissance the feudal system became outmoded and passed from use. Paper, printing and the mariner's compass came into the knowledge of many men. Explorers visited new continents and wrote accounts of their discoveries for all who could read. Copernicus, a Polish astronomer (1473–1543), insisted that the sun, not the earth, was the center of the solar system—the first great advance in astronomy since the days of Egypt. Again man began to study, to speculate, to experiment along scientific lines. Newton, an English mathematician (1642–1727), established basic laws from which the science of engineering grew and prospered.

And, during the Renaissance, once again wheeled

vehicles appeared on the streets and roads. Carriage builders and wheelwrights were touched by a new, creative urge. By 1550 Paris had three coaches, all belonging to royalty. The wheelwright Walter Rippon built the first coach made in England—for the Earl of Rutland. The next year he built one for Queen Mary. One William Boonen brought a coach from Holland for Queen Elizabeth and became her coachman. Early carriages were for royalty and the rich.

Then came the first "jitneys," or, as vehicles for hire were called, "hackney coaches." In 1635, because of traffic congestion, London limited their number to fifty. Twenty-five years later the law permitted only three hundred. Simultaneously coaches grew in size and could accommodate six, eight, or more passengers. Before long the vehicles ran on regularly established routes. For the first time since the days of Julius Caesar (100–44 B.C.), the general public enjoyed closed stages running on definite routes and schedules.

But the power that drove the wheels still was horse-power in the flesh. In this respect the early modern age differed little from the days of the ancients.

However, beginning with the Renaissance and continuing even to the present, a new day for trade, transportation and the home was dawning, and invention was the sun that brought it in. Invention has been described as the stuff of which civilization is made because its incalculable effects upon man's activities, thoughts and feelings mold his life. Discovery leads to innovation, and innovation leads to discovery. The chain is endless. Ultimately invention revolutionizes man's thoughts, actions, his very life.

In his workshop Leonardo da Vinci, famed Florentine painter (1452–1519), constructed a block and tackle—the first application of the lever since Archimedes! He described, in addition, an aeolipile, shaped liked a huge head which spouted vapor from its mouth—the first recorded experiment with steam since the ancient Hero!

In a treatise on pneumatics, Giovanni della Porta, Italian philosopher (about 1538–1615), pointed out that a vacuum could be created by condensing steam. Denis Papin, French inventor (1647–1714), suggested that the condensation of steam could be employed to make a vacuum under a piston. And in 1698 Thomas Savery, English inventor, built the earliest steam engine in practical form—used to pump water out of coal mines. From other equally rich minds came inventions of tools and machines of incredible ingenuity.

So dawns the Age of Invention. Comes the steam engine, the Age of Steam. Steam revolutionizes transportation, brings on the Railroad Age, the Steamboat Age.

Comes the invention of textile machinery, the springboard for the Industrial Revolution and the Machine Age. Comes the discovery of oil drilling, of the metallurgical processes that convert iron into steel, of gas and diesel engines—each so revolutionary in its impact upon the world that it calls forth such designations as the Oil Age, the Steel Age, the Diesel Age.

From successive inventions, discoveries and innovations, new industries spring into being. In each field, inevitably one man builds on the accumulated knowledge of the discoverers and experimenters who have gone before. By his own ingenuity, energy and ability this man inspires the birth, shapes the destiny of a new industry. Such men have changed our world.

- 2 -

JAMES WATT

1736 - 1819

FATHER OF THE STEAM ENGINE

In MANY RESPECTS the world into which James Watt was born, January 19, 1736, was a shabby place. The numbing effects of the long Dark Ages still lingered. Actually, however, life was dynamic and sparkled with vitality, creative energy and adventurous spirit. For the curiosity and labor of great scientists, engineers, inventors, writers, statesmen and sturdy merchants were already establishing the world forces of today's culture and progress.

James Watt, who gladdened the family of a small merchant in Greenock, Scotland, was to become one of the greatest inventors of his day and of all time. But his success came only after years of struggle and discouragement.

Watt's darkest hour came in 1771. Two years previously he had patented a steam engine, and in return for the cost of building the apparatus he had turned over two thirds of any profits to Dr. John Roebuck, proprietor of the Carron Iron Works. But Roebuck had fallen upon hard times, and now, by order of the London Court of Bankruptcy, his effects were going under the hammer. From the shadows at the back of the room James Watt— thin, shabby and pinch-faced—anxiously listened to the proceedings.

Finally the king's auctioneer put up for sale an odd piece of machinery which he called a "fire engine."

"What am I bid, gentlemen? Who starts it off?" To humor his audience, the king's auctioneer painted a fanciful picture of Watt's invention. "The greatest pumping engine of all time! Newcomen's engine can't hold a candle to it! And a two-thirds interest in all the profits goes with it. Why, every mine in Cornwall will want Mr. Watt's fire engine. Your chance, gentlemen, or Mr. Watt gets back his full rights—and all the profits!"

Everybody laughed. No one bid. Not one of Roebuck's creditors considered the steam engine worth a farthing. Watt turned away despairingly. Later he wrote his wife that invention was futile. And when he returned home he followed her advice and turned to civil engineering. Years of effort had left him with unsalable rights to an unsalable engine.

Watt had labored long and hard over his steam engine. At nineteen he was apprenticed to a London instrument maker. He found the work difficult and exacting, the hours long. His wages barely bought him food. After a year his health broke, and he was sent home. He was not out of work long.

Close to Greenock, the three-hundred-year-old Glasgow University, standing on a beautiful campus on High Street, needed a handyman. Young Watt became "mathematical instrument maker to the university."

At the time Joseph Black, later to discover latent heat, was lecturing on chemistry at Glasgow, and John Robison, later professor of natural philosophy at Edinburgh University, was a student. Lost in fascination, Watt listened to the theories of steam as propounded by scientist and scholar. Sometimes, daringly, he contributed ideas of his own.

Soon Watt was obsessed with the idea of building a steam engine. For six years he carried on experiments in his college workshop. He got nowhere.

Watt had a foundation to build on. For over half a century British mineowners had been using a steam-pumping engine invented by Thomas Newcomen, a blacksmith of Dartmouth. Consisting of a separate boiler and engine, the apparatus used artificial means to condense steam. Actually, Newcomen's engine was little more than a crude pump which burned so much coal that it was impractical except at collieries where fuel was plentiful and cheap.

In the college's collection of scientific apparatus was a model of the Newcomen engine. One day a professor asked Watt to repair it. The handyman took the engine apart, put it together, studied its operation and was struck by its enormous consumption of coal. He set himself to discover a remedy.

Many of us recall the picture in our schoolbooks of James Watt sitting before a stove and watching a boiling kettle spouting steam. Though imaginary, the picture typifies Watt, a man who used his head as well as his hands. To remedy the defects of the Newcomen engine, he began a scientific study of the properties of steam. He tried to discover the relationship of steam's density and pressure to its temperature. He concluded that the two conditions were essential to the economic use of steam in a condensing steam engine.

Fairly obsessed by such problems, Watt often was seen wandering about the campus lost in thought. While strolling under tall, blossoming trees one Sabbath afternoon in the spring of 1765, the idea struck him. A separate condenser!

Here is the story as told by Watt himself: "I had entered the green and passed the old washing house. I was thinking of the engine at the time. I had gone as far as the herd's house when the idea came into my mind that as steam was an elastic body it would rush into a vacuum and if a connection were made between the cylinder and an exhausting vessel, it might there be condensed without cooling the cylinder. . . . I had not walked farther than the golf-house when the whole thing was arranged in my mind." His concept was basic to the development of an engine which would convert a new power—steam— to the useful purposes of mankind.

Watt's efforts to apply the theory of the separate condenser and to build the necessary parts make up a story of exacting toil and frequent frustration. Not until January 1769—four years after his original idea—did he receive his first patent.

But the inventor's strivings to demonstrate the merits

of his idea put him in debt even before he could produce
an engine. He agreed, therefore, to give two thirds of
the profits from his invention to John Roebuck, founder
of the Carron Iron Works, in return for backing and facilities of the ironmaster. So, at last, his steam engine
became a tangible fact.

Then, at the auction of Roebuck's effects, Watt's hopes
had been dashed. He got back his engine and renounced
invention.

Watt secured a job as a surveyor and showed such
ability that his services on canal and harbor projects
were in great demand. But he was an inventor at heart.
He originated a simple surveyor's micrometer for measuring distances. And he could not forget his engine, now
in his possession and slowly gathering rust. Constantly,
new ideas gnawed at his mind.

In due course Watt met Matthew Boulton, a wealthy,
strong-minded man with a good business head, and
owner of the Soho Engineering Works at Birmingham.
For two thirds of the profits, Boulton agreed to take a
chance on financing the engine. The two founded the
firm of Boulton & Watt.

To the great satisfaction of the partners, the Watt engine was built and proved workable. But how to convince the mineowners and others that the Watt steam
engine would do the work of many horses? The inventor
hit on a way. He would interpret claims for his engine in
terms of "horsepower."

Using strong dray horses, he made calculations and
measurements. In one minute, he found, a horse would

lift 33,000 pounds through a distance of one foot. One horsepower, then, was 33,000 foot-pounds per minute. On that basis his engine could do the work of forty horses.

Boulton was a good salesman. He snatched at the new unit of measurement and used Watt's horsepower calculations to sell the engine to mine owners. They bought.

So superior was Watt's engine that, by 1783, it had displaced all but one of the Newcomen engines in Cornwall mines.

Watt's engine was no slow-working, cumbrous and fuel-wasting pumping engine. His first invention made the steam engine quick, powerful and efficient. But he kept on inventing, improving his engine so it could drive all kinds of machinery.

Though Watt was not the first to invent a steam engine, he *was* the man who showed the method and developed the appliance that put the vapor of boiling water into the universal service of mankind.

With a succession of patents following his first, he gave the steam engine its modern mechanical details and its purpose. Except for his use of the old-time beam and his persistence in sticking to low pressure, Watt's engine might be called modern.

Then, too, his improvements in the utilization of steam power and in the complicated knowledge of the composition of steam were fundamental. He invented the centrifugal governor which automatically controlled the speed of rotative engines. And he originated the indicator which, as the stroke proceeded, drew a diagram of the relation of the steam's pressure to its volume—the steam engineer's "stethoscope."

In the realm of pure science Watt is recognized as the discoverer of the composition of water.

Aided by improvements in its product and by advances in knowledge, the business of Boulton & Watt prospered.

In January 1796—twenty-five years after the Roebuck auction—the partners dedicated a new foundry. Said Boulton to Boswell, the biographer, on an occasion when he visited the Soho Works, "I sell here, sir, what all the world desires to have—power!"

Giving his share of the business to his sons, James and Gregory, Watt retired in 1800. A man of insight and of warm friendships, in his many surviving letters Watt tells his own achievements with modesty and dry humor.

Never could he quite stop applying himself to the occupation he once had called "futile"—invention. His last idea was a machine for copying sculpture. Shortly before his death Watt copied busts with this device and presented them to his friends as the "work of a young artist just entering his eighty-third year." He died August 19, 1819.

Until the arrival of steam the muscles of man and beast supplied all power, except for the water wheel and the windmill. Watt put steam power to work to drive all kinds of mechanisms, to supplant and relieve man's sore muscles and aching back and the beast's heavy burden. Nothing like it had occurred in the history of the world. And once his engine had taken hold, there was no stopping steam.

Thereafter man had not only wind and water as primary power for the machines he invented, but also steam. Long, dark years of drudgery and toil ended as engines and machines began to ease his daily life.

Now man builds thousands upon thousands of engines, many of them giant affairs. As he first put mechanical horsepower to work, he multiplied his units and increased their heaviness. Then he learned to decrease the weight of his engines.

Soon he discovered electricity, thus finding a way to diminish the number of units. He harnessed power resources to develop electricity. In single plants he built unheard-of horsepower, proportionately reducing manual and mechanical slavery and labor. By the early twentieth century a single steam turbine did the work of 837,000 horses, of 5,000,000 slaves!

If steam could drive stationary machines, why couldn't it drive carriage and wagon wheels? Fantastic but fascinating thought! But man can dream!

At first the dream was limited to a vehicle on rails, probably because steam engines originally found use in collieries. The thought was of an engine to replace the donkeys that pulled coal rail cars or the horse-driven rail lines which were beginning to compete with stagecoaches.

In less than ten years the dream came true. The steam locomotive, invented and tried out in England and America, made horses obsolete on the rail routes and stagecoach lines.

And people who, a few years before, skeptically had watched Fitch and Fulton display their frightening steamboats, now gathered courage to cross the seas in steam-driven vessels.

Steam's effect on horse rail lines and stagecoach routes was but a forerunner of even greater changes—first, the steam-driven "horseless carriage," ancestor of the automobile, then the gas engine, which in its cylinder substituted an explosion of gas for the thrust of steam.

In transportation, steam smashed down the barriers of isolation. In production, steam powered new machines and entire new industries.

If John Roebuck's creditors only had known! Within their grasp, at the auction of his effects, was an invention worth all of the money in England. By default they returned the steam engine to its inventor, James Watt. With it he helped revolutionize the world.

- 3 -

RICHARD ARKWRIGHT

1732 - 1792

FATHER OF THE INDUSTRIAL REVOLUTION

RICHARD ARKWRIGHT was born at Preston, Lancashire, England, in 1732, and from his modest home he began life humbly. A thirteenth son, in his thirteenth year he was apprenticed to a barber at Bolton, and for thirteen years thereafter he shaved the faces and trimmed the beards of hard-working farmers and townsmen. A small beginning for a man destined to play the major part in the Industrial Revolution!

Many of Arkwright's neighbors—women and children as well as men—not only worked at their regular jobs but also were part-time spinners or weavers.

With England's population growing by leaps and bounds, the demand for cloth was unlimited. Every family among the Lancashire farmers spun for the weavers, and many houses even had their own loom-chamber or loom-house in the back yard.

For making their cloth, the hand-loom weavers had to use a woolen or linen warp imported from India and Ireland, the spun cotton yarn being suitable only for weft or filling. Thus expensive wool and linen were added to the cost of clothes.

The spinners and weavers in the homes "rose with the lark" and labored late by candlelight. Every minute of the day that they could spare from their farm or household chores they spent at their spinning wheels or looms. Most were tenant farmers not far removed from serfdom. For their farm labor they received little or nothing; for their yarn and cloth, a mere pittance.

Even with their combined income they could not afford to buy the cloth they were making. But Lancashire was the busiest county in all England, fast gaining a reputation for its manufactured cloths and hosiery.

The eternal problem was how to produce more weft, how to speed up the spinning wheel. Spinners with inventive minds and talented hands tinkered with their wheels, and rumors of secret improvements and new devices were rife.

The barber of Bolton picked up much gossip of "spindles, shuttles, wheels, and contrivances," to quote Thomas Carlyle. "In stropping razors, in shaving dirty beards, and in the contradictions and confusions attendant thereon, the man had notions in that rough head of his." For Arkwright was a bit of a tinkerer himself.

When he was twice thirteen he became a wigmaker, in which trade he showed his inventive genius by origi-

nating a new method of dyeing hair and preparing it for wigs. He traveled widely to buy hair for his wigs from the heads of poor farmers' daughters.

On one of these expeditions Arkwright, of whom Carlyle also wrote: "He was a plain, almost gross, bag-cheeked, pot-bellied Lancashireman, with an air of painful reflection, yet also of copious, free digestion," won a country lass and brought her back to Bolton as his wife. She proved to be ambitious, extravagant and somewhat shrewish. But Arkwright was proud of his possession of her and did not mind her extravagance, for he was prospering.

Chancing through Standhill, Lancashire, in 1767, Arkwright heard the spinners had raided the home of James Hargreaves, himself a spinner of humble origin, rightly suspected of having a device that gave him an advantage over them.

Hargreaves' invention had come about by accident. One day his daughter Jenny, in a childish prank overturned his spinning wheel. It fell in such a way that the spindle, ordinarily horizontal, was vertical. It continued to revolve, and the poor spinner thought, "Why not a series of vertical spindles, mechanically connected, so that a number of threads can be spun at the same time?"

With eight vertical spindles, Hargreaves' "jenny"—as it came to be called after the inventor's daughter—was the first device to spin more than one thread simultaneously. At one stroke he increased his production eight times. Small wonder that he could not keep his secret! His great output of yarn roused the suspicions and fury of the spinners. They raided his house and wrecked his contraption. After that Hargreaves left Standhill for Nottingham.

Whether or not the traveling buyer of hair saw Hargreaves' "spinning jenny" in Standhill in 1767 is not known, but at this time, as Carlyle puts it, "certain notions in Dick Arkwright's head did at last bring to bear." He gave up his wig business to try his hand at building a spinning machine.

Once Arkwright had made up his mind, he poured all his thought, effort and money into his project. As his money dwindled away, the extravagant Mistress Arkwright scolded and implored. Finally, in a rage, she deliberately smashed the inventor's precious model. At the sight of the wreckage her formerly meek husband turned on her and drove her from the house.

Arkwright then employed John Kay, watchmaker of Warrington, to assist him in the construction of a new model. Reviving old ideas of spinning by rollers—said to have been conceived thirty years before by Thomas Highs—and imitating Hargreaves' idea of vertical spindles, Arkwright advanced the spinning wheel to a machine which not only gave the multiple production of Hargreaves' jenny but also made a superior, strong, hard yarn.

On July 3, 1769, Arkwright received his first spinning wheel patent, and he, too, moved to Nottingham, a hosiery center.

A year later Hargreaves came into the open and patented his machine. His spinning jennies attained

great popularity and outnumbered Arkwright's for almost a quarter of a century. They were built with 20
spindles, then 50 and 60, then as many as 120. But Hargreaves did not live to see the success of his invention,
or to profit by it. He died on a poor farm in 1778.

Meanwhile, with capital furnished by the Messrs.
Wright, bankers, Arkwright erected his first mill at Nottingham, introducing for the first time spinning machinery run by horsepower rather than by hand. But
there were "bugs" in his machine. Operation was so
costly that Messrs. Wright withdrew from the project.

Untutored, wheezing under his three hundred pounds
of weight and from chronic asthma, gross of face and
manner, Arkwright refused to quit. He had natural
sagacity, tireless energy and a contagious faith in himself. He kept his mill going. And so convincingly did he
talk to Jedediah Strutt that the wealthy hosiery manufacturer of Derby and his partner, Samuel Need, entered
into partnership with Arkwright.

Flowing through Belfer, Derbyshire, was a water
stream. On its banks Arkwright, with his new partners,
built a second mill, much bigger than the first. He abandoned horsepower in the flesh and utilized water power,
thus giving the Arkwright machine its lasting name—the
Arkwright spinning water frame.

With harder twist, supplied by water power, England's yarn now could be used for warp as well as weft
—a revolutionary development. This made it possible
for the weaver to dispense with imported linen or
woolen warp and to make all-cotton cloth.

In 1773 England, therefore, could boast the manufacture of the first cotton cloth properly so called and could undersell the cloth of other nations.

So great was the demand for genuine, cheap cotton cloth that Arkwright and Strutt (Need having retired) erected another large mill, this at Comford, and still another at Milford.

Driving at top speed behind four horses, Arkwright constantly shuttled among his mills. His supervision began on the first day of construction and continued unceasingly through his years of daily management. He was a mountain of a man who severely tested the springs of the carriage builder. In 1781 Arkwright and Strutt dissolved their partnership, the former retaining all but one mill.

Arkwright secured several spinning wheel patents after his first. That he envisioned his invention as having revolutionary social and economic promise for England and the English people is shown by the wording of his first patent. He claimed to have invented a machine "which would be of great utility to a great many manufacturers, as well as to His Majesty's subjects in general, by employing a great number of poor people in working the said machinery."

Arkwright's Comford Mill marked the beginning of the factory system. From far and near men and women left their homes to lodge or board near the mill. Even children were apprenticed under a bond of service for stated periods. The productive capacity of the mill was fabulous.

As early as 1776, the inventor employed over five thousand people in his various mills. Wherever an Arkwright factory sprang up other factories were built—a "manufacturing center" came into being.

Not that the hand spinners did not fight him. Inevitably mobs attacked every mill that Arkwright erected. But inevitably there to restrain them—if he could reach the spot in time—was the giant of a man who had come out of poverty himself. He could answer the harangue of the mob in its own tongue, the jargon of the illiterate Lancashireman.

Never did Arkwright hesitate to subject himself to the rage of those who could see him only as a monster taking bread from their mouths. When he built one of the first steam-driven spinning mills at Chorley, a mob burned it to the ground. Arkwright was rebuilding it before the ashes were cold. The spinners were slow to accept Arkwright's argument that he was giving work to the poor. But they could do little against the fateful change he had started.

Inevitably the handworkers' purpose—to hold back machine progress—was doomed to failure.

The system of spinning and weaving in the home waned. Slowly but surely the system of working in cotton mills and factories with frames and looms under one roof prevailed. Gradually opposition to machines abated. The hand spinners realized that, instead of taking work from them, machines gave more jobs to more people by making things cheaper so that more people could purchase them.

Before the Arkwright water frame England was far behind her sister nations of western and southern Europe in making cotton into fabrics. She was a heavy importer of cloths which were expensive and beyond the purse of most of her people. But by 1790 she was supplying her home demand and, in addition, was exporting British cotton cloth to the tune of $7,500,000 annually.

The new cloths were cheap and available. For the first time the British people could clothe themselves properly. No longer was decent and healthful clothing limited to expensive imported silks and woolen fabrics which only the rich could afford.

So Arkwright's spinning frame truly proved itself "of great utility to His Majesty's subjects in general, by employing a great many poor people." It created other enterprises. And additional jobs increased buying power to give Britain unheard-of prosperity.

As an inventor Arkwright overflowed with ardor to perfect his machine. He showed tremendous courage in facing mobs, in holding to his purpose. He systematized his factories and offices. Working from five in the morning till nine at night, his energy was boundless. He was a "successful man." What more could he wish?

Much more. Late in life he became conscious of his lack of education, and after office hours he devoted an hour a day to studying grammar and another to improving his writing.

Arkwright's claim to be the inventor of the spinning frame was challenged in sensational patent suits. With characteristic vigor he fought his enemies. Losing the first time, he won his second case, and his claims were declared valid. But the controversy raged long after his death and continues today.

Whatever may be the truth of the matter, the fact

remains that Arkwright set in motion a series of events that changed the face of the western world.

For with his spinning water frame Arkwright touched off the Industrial Revolution. And revolution it was. Until the accomplishment of this barber-wigmaker turned inventor, the material culture of the world scarcely had changed from that of primitive man.

Until Arkwright's time western Europe held to much the same industrial techniques as the peoples who lived five thousand years before. Most of the aspects of manufacturing—preparing cereal, making bread, and, certainly, spinning and weaving—man had known and utilized as far back as history goes. From the Stone Age to the steam engine and spinning machinery, only two improvements in material culture had been outstanding —utilizing metals and developing navigation to a science. Life still was largely agricultural. But the Industrial Revolution, sparked by Richard Arkwright, changed society, ushered in a new era for man, eased his work and reduced drudgery in his home.

In 1786 Arkwright—rich, residing at Willersley Castle and high sheriff of the county—was visited by King George III only a few days after an attempt had been made upon the monarch's life. The king, in recognition of Arkwright's contributions, rewarded him with a knighthood.

Six years later Sir Richard Arkwright died in his sleep at the age of sixty. One wonders if, with all his vision, he fully realized before his death the miracle he had wrought.

- (4) -

SAMUEL SLATER

1768 - 1835

FATHER OF THE AMERICAN TEXTILE INDUSTRY

FOR YEARS the American colonists of the eighteenth century heard little of great industrial changes which were occurring back in the "old country"—a revolution growing around two machine inventions, James Hargreaves' spinning jenny and Richard Arkwright's spinning water frame. When rumors about England's new cotton machinery finally began to reach the Americans, they were absorbed in fighting their War for Independence.

With their political freedom won, the hardy founders of the United States faced the equally important task of throwing off their new nation's commercial dependence on Great Britain. As one means to that end they saw the necessity of overtaking England in spinning and weaving.

Many Americans tried to reproduce spinning ma-

chines. Repeatedly they failed. And England did not intend to lose a good thing. By law she had forbidden the export of machine parts or plans, and thus discouraged the emigration of skilled mechanics.

Secretly, however, one Samuel Slater, a British apprentice workman, determined to reach "the land of opportunity."

Samuel Slater, son of a well-to-do farmer, was born at Holly House Farm, Belper, Derbyshire, June 9, 1768. "Samuel not only writes well and is good at figures, but is also a decided mechanical genius," his parent observed when, thriftily, he decided to apprentice his son.

At nearby Milford, Jedediah Strutt, a partner of Richard Arkwright, operated a large textile plant, and to him Samuel, a strapping lad of fifteen, was bound for six and a half years. His father's pride was justified. Well schooled and sharing the advantages of a prosperous home, Samuel also was ambitious. So well did he learn his trade that before his term was half over he was an overseer.

Yet he yearned for America and chafed under his long apprenticeship. Secretly reading public prints from the United States, he learned of the numerous offers current there to encourage the development of the textile machinery which was so sorely desired. Honorably, he would complete his contract. Then he would act!

At last Slater finished his term of instruction. Having read in a Philadelphia newspaper that the Pennsylvania legislature had paid a £100 bounty to a worker for devising repair parts for Hargreaves' jennies—only to receive imperfect mechanisms—he needed no further incentive. Somehow, he would get to Philadelphia!

Samuel's mother, widowed the year before, had been left in comfortable circumstances, and an elder brother, William, was helping to run Holly House Farm and care for the younger children. With a clear conscience, but fearing to tell even his mother, the twenty-one-year-old mechanic disguised himself as a farmer, took the long-anticipated step and boarded a vessel for America.

After sixty-six days of storm and becalmed seas, one blustery day in November 1789 the impatient youth finally jumped ashore at a North River dock in New York.

Within four days he obtained employment from the New York Manufacturing Society, which had a cotton factory near the waterfront. For, though he had no drawings of the textile machines he knew so well, he had sewed in his coat lining his apprentice papers—proof that he had worked on machinery so badly needed in America.

One day, while wandering along the North River docks, Slater fell in with a packet captain from Providence, Rhode Island. The chance acquaintance told him that one Moses Brown, a retired Quaker of means, had started a cotton factory at Pawtucket and was having trouble with his machines.

Slater wrote to Brown, "If I do not make as good a yarn as they do in England, I will have nothing for my services, but will throw the whole of what I have attempted over the border."

Brown liked his spirit and summoned him to Pawtucket.

Slater's only fear was that mechanics with the necessary skill to help him build the intricate machinery might not be available. Thereupon Brown introduced him to Orziel Wilkinson, also a Quaker, who, with four husky sons, ran a nearby machine shop and iron foundry. "If anybody in the world can help thee, it is Orziel and his boys," Brown said.

Nevertheless, when the young Englishman first saw Brown's poor little mill and its "worthless machinery" —so unlike the great Derbyshire factories of his boyhood —he "felt disheartened," as the good Quaker later wrote.

The hospitable Wilkinsons, all keen and intelligent, though none of them had enjoyed schooling, took as a boarder the cultured, polished and likable Englishman. He and the boys—Abraham and Isaac, twins, and David and Daniel—became fast friends. Soon, indeed, Samuel was "another son" to Orziel, for he fell in love with Hannah, his daughter, and married her within a year.

Thanks to the excellent, hard-working mechanics, the Wilkinsons, Slater's worries about getting his machines built vanished. *Fashioning the parts entirely from memory*, Samuel Slater completely equipped the mill with Arkwright machinery. On December 20, 1790—only thirteen months after he had landed in New York—the test was ready. As the young Englishman and Moses Brown anxiously watched, the machines "hummed sweetly to work."

This 72-spindle mill at Pawtucket, Rhode Island, was

America's first successful textile factory and marked the beginning of modern industry in the nation.

Fourteen months after Slater had perfected his machine, Moses Brown wrote to Secretary of the Treasury Alexander Hamilton that within a year sufficient machinery and mills could be erected to supply the whole United States with domestic yarn. Imported yarn would be a need of the past!

Indeed, after a while the productivity of Slater's mill began to frighten the worthy Moses Brown. For within two years Slater had accumulated 2000 pounds of yarn, and the cautious and thrifty Quaker told his protégé, "Thee must shut down thy gates or thee will spin all my farms into cotton yarn."

Samuel Slater became a manufacturer on his own, and also built mills in partnership with David Wilkinson and others for years. His first mill at Pawtucket proved so inadequate that three years later he built a new one, and then later others elsewhere.

Using these factories for training men to build textile machinery as well as for production, by 1809 he and his partner had ringed Providence with seventeen mills possessing 14,290 spindles. A few years later Slater expanded his mill holdings throughout New England.

As early as December 1791, Secretary of the Treasury Hamilton, in his famous *Report on Manufactures,* had remarked on Slater's success. Arkwright machines had crossed the Atlantic and were operating in Rhode Island!

"The Manufactory at Pawtucket," the Secretary wrote to Congress, "has the merit of being the first in introducing into the United States the celebrated cotton mill which not only furnished materials for the manufactory itself but for the supply of private families for household manufactures."

Just as Arkwright with his spinning water frame had touched off the Industrial Revolution in Britain, so Slater with the same machine repeated the miracle in America. New England textile mills, which used only 500 bales of cotton yearly in 1800, called for 90,000 bales only fifteen years later, and new or related industries were springing up alongside the textile plants.

In 1836 George S. White, in his *Memoir of Samuel Slater*, called the man who had built from memory a mill full of machinery the "father of American manufactures."

But Slater did not found the new American textile industry without overcoming difficulties. In the two decades following his first mill, French and English fabrics had flooded the nation's markets. Even the War of 1812 failed to shut out imports, and the sudden peace found the markets glutted. So disarranged were the infant home establishments that only a few weathered the storm.

"To the undaunted perseverance of those few establishments," White wrote, "we owe the present progress and triumph of our improved manufactures. By the introduction of the best and latest machinery, and with the advantages of New England water power, they have survived every attack, surmounted every obstacle, and overcome every difficulty."

The successful introduction of the young Englishman's mill, accomplished "by unwavering firmness," might teach us, White continued, "not to despise the day of small things"—for Slater had begun with only seventy-two spindles.

Even by the time that White wrote his *Memoir*, Irish linen and India cottons, which once had supplied American markets, were little known. They had been supplanted by cloths made in the U.S.A., priced to fit everybody's pocketbook. "An immense quantity of our cotton cloths are sold at very low price, and are consumed in all parts of the Union. . . . Large exportations are made to South America where they are in high repute and have driven the British and India goods out. . . ." Slater lived to see these astonishing developments.

Tall, erect, well proportioned and effortlessly carrying his two hundred and sixty pounds, Samuel Slater had regular, handsome features and a ruddy complexion. Before her death in 1812, Hannah Wilkinson blessed him with ten sons, six of whom lived to manhood. Three of them carried on his extensive business.

After becoming an American, Slater eagerly sent to Derbyshire for his entire family. Arriving in 1803, his brother John traveled the country on horseback, seeking sites for textile mills along promising streams. In 1823 the brothers jointly operated mills at Jewett, Connecticut, and in 1831 Samuel conveyed his interest in the property to John, who operated it until his death.

Slater's mother and his older brother William, however, remained on Holly House Farm. Though Slater never again crossed the Atlantic he corresponded regularly with his mother, often writing that his health, the great number of his concerns and his "concentrative-ness" bound him to America.

One of the mills, located by John near Smithfield, Rhode Island, became the site of Slatersville. Another, established in 1811 in Worcester County, Massachusetts, became the town of Webster—named by Slater for Daniel Webster, whom he greatly admired.

Though retaining his Pawtucket citizenship until his death, Slater spent most of his last years in a mansion that he had built at East Webster. Here, on April 21, 1835, he died. In the little cemetery on the Slater grounds a plain shaft of Quincy granite marks the resting place of the father of the American textile industry —the immigrant boy who built even better than he knew —and from memory.

America's first industry—the textile industry—owes its birth to Samuel Slater, and from his day to the present it has ranked as one of the nation's foremost.

Textile machinery first harnessed spinning frames and looms to the rocky streams of New England and then to the more placid rivers of the cotton-growing South and Middle West. Mill sites became towns, towns became cities, and an agricultural nation became an industrial nation. Transportation by land and sea and countless stores and businesses grew and thrived as a result of the whirring spindles, the clattering looms and the rumbling pulleys and shaftings introduced by Samuel Slater.

With all of the young Englishman's competence and perseverance, when he sailed for America, carrying the plans for Arkwright's spinning frame in his head, little did he suspect that his personal success story would grow to the dynamic success story of an entire nation!

Or did he? When Slater was a boy he saw similar changes occurring in Devonshire and Lancashire—towns growing around mills, country folk becoming city dwellers, an agricultural people converting to an industrial nation. And Belper, Slater's birthplace, was but a stone's throw from Bolton, where Arkwright first saw light of day. The teeming environment of Samuel's youth abounded with evidence of his predecessor's fabulous success. Whether or not Slater dreamed that he and Arkwright would revolutionize the western world, that was what they did!

- 5 -

DAVID WILKINSON

1771 - 1852

FATHER OF THE MACHINE TOOL INDUSTRY

WHEN JAMES WATT, with his steam engine, and Richard Arkwright, with his spinning water frame, sired the Industrial Revolution in the eighteenth century in England, they set off a series of chainlike reactions in industry and invention. One vital link in the chain was an entirely new demand for accurate tools with which to fashion parts for increasingly complex steam engines and textile machines.

In England an array of brilliant British mechanics met the challenge. Among them, John Wilkinson, Joseph Bramah, Samuel Bentham, Henry Maudslay, Marc I. Brunel and James Nasmyth—to name the most notable —produced the tools for the dawning Machine Age.

All were inventors. All attained wealth, and Bentham and Brunel were knighted for their achievements.

47

In contrast to England, how sorry was contemporary mechanical progress in the scattered, sparsely peopled settlements of America! The "mother country" wanted it that way, for in her colonies she discouraged the use of machines and the establishment of industries.

Yet long before the American Revolution little iron foundries and forges dotted New England's forests and farms. And the adage that "necessity is the mother of invention" never had truer application than in those crude workshops. For farmer-mechanics made the necessary axes, scythes and plows, and village smiths shod horses, repaired wagons, mended heavy looms and wrought the badly needed nails and edged tools. With sledge and anvil these men hammered the term "Yankee ingenuity" into the English language. Many of them handed down their craftsmanship from generation to generation.

When the Revolutionary War raged, these ingenious Yankees helped the American cause by casting and boring cannon and by meeting the desperate demand for stands of arms for our hard-pressed soldiers. Finally the country was free. No longer was Britain able to stifle the long-standing American urge for the tools and machines which would make the nation industrially self-sufficient. Then the shops of the pioneer mechanics became the seeds of American industries. Typical mechanics of Yankee ingenuity were the Wilkinsons.

A few years before the Revolutionary War, Orziel Wilkinson, a Quaker, operated a blacksmith and screw-cutting machine shop at Smithfield, Rhode Island. His four sons—Abraham and Isaac, twins, and David and

Daniel—inherited their father's mechanical ability. Indeed, at an early age, the third son, David, showed marked genius.

David Wilkinson first saw the light of day in Smithfield, January 5, 1771. In his *Reminiscences* he recalls as one of his first memories his father's placing him astride a log to work a stirrup press for heading nails.

When Orziel moved to Pawtucket, Rhode Island, to establish an anchor forge, David, a lad of twelve, was "quite an expert in wielding the sledge." David Wilkinson used to say that he was "graduated" from school at nine. For the little red schoolhouse which he attended burned down, and he never went back.

A giant in stature, restless, indeed "eager after knowledge," David traveled up and down the rivers to and from iron foundries and mines and various mills of Connecticut and Massachusetts in connection with the business of the Wilkinson shop.

Some people say David Wilkinson invented the steamboat. Returning home from the Hope Furnace at Scituate and stopping to see the ore bed in Cranston, he engaged in conversation a young mechanic named Ormsbee, who was repairing a Boulton & Watt steam engine. The upshot was that the two young mechanics installed the engine in a hired boat, David designing the paddle wheels and connecting mechanism. They ran the vessel three and a half miles from Winsor's Cove to Providence. This was in 1794. Robert Fulton's historic boat, the *Clermont*, also employing paddles, didn't begin to ply the Hudson until 1807.

But Wilkinson himself scarcely took his "invention of the steamboat" seriously. "After our frolic was over, being short of funds," he reminisced, "we hauled the boat up and gave it over."

The following year, when he was twenty-three, David became interested in making a machine to cut iron screws on their centers, thus to make them more perfect. He designed and built a sliding rest lathe for turning iron and brass.

No accurate description of Wilkinson's lathe remains, but from the almost simultaneous invention of the sliding rest lathe in England and America we know that it revolutionized mechanical work, machining and machines. The old lathe, with its stationary rest, left all control to the dexterity of the hand and the correctness of the eye. A time killer, it was exceedingly costly to operate, and its finished jobs were of unequal quality.

With the sliding rest lathe, not the workman but the rest itself held the cutting tool. It slid along the surface of the bench, holding a direction parallel with the axis of the work, thus enabling the tool to fashion the most delicate or most ponderous pieces of metal or machinery with precision and speed.

In 1798—four years after he had produced his machine at his father's plant—David secured a patent. However, fresh interests had seized the eager youth, and, although the sliding rest lathe came into wide use, he did not try to protect his patent.

But the real turning point in David Wilkinson's life had occurred in 1789 when a young Englishman, Samuel

Slater, came to live in the Wilkinson family. Samuel had brought to America *in his head* the plans of Arkwright's complicated spinning water frame. With the Wilkinsons' expert help, the immigrant installed the spinning machines in Moses Brown's little Pawtucket mill—the plant that launched the manufacturing industry in the United States.

In constructing Arkwright's machinery for the new nation's first textile mill, enormous mechanical difficulties had to be overcome and David became Slater's "hands."

"I forged the iron work, and turned (that is, fashioned) the rollers and spindles, in part," Wilkinson wrote. "All turning was done with hand tools, and by hand power, with crank wheels."

The machine shops of the Wilkinsons became part and parcel of Slater's textile mills, which began to spread out over New England. Not only did the Wilkinsons make the machinery for him but they kept it in repair and provided new parts.

But that wasn't all. Always the Wilkinsons needed more and more apprentices. Their shops became training schools for toolmakers. Soon skilled "Wilkinson men" were in demand. They followed the new textile factories which sprang up like mushrooms along New England's heady rivers and streams. Many, encouraged by David, established their own shops in the new communities which grew up near the plants.

Thus Wilkinson fostered the budding machine tool industry which had its birth in the machine needs of the cotton mills and of the arms plants and arsenals.

As the years passed and the textile industry grew, Pawtucket prospered and, with it, Sam Slater and David Wilkinson. The latter, though unschooled, became a man of great intellectual attainment, learning by experience, travel and observation. "He gathered the wheat into the garner and gave the chaff to the whirlwind." He was known and esteemed by many of the great of his day.

But during the depression of 1829 Wilkinson suffered reverses and was compelled to give up his machine tool business in Pawtucket. He moved his family to Cohoes Falls, New York, where he engaged in textile manufacturing and became prominent in the community's early progress and social life.

But only for a few years. Again he suffered reverses. After 1836, the aging Wilkinson worked as a laborer on bridge, canal and river projects in the United States and Canada. "Wherever I could find anything to do, I went. And it is wonderful how I endured exposure to wet and cold."

Not until February 3, 1852, at the age of eighty-one, did death overtake him at Caledonia Springs, Ontario, Canada. His remains were returned to Pawtucket, the scene of his historical triumphs, and entombed in the family vault.

Recording memories of his late friend, the Reverend George Taft in 1865 summed up David Wilkinson as follows: "One of nature's noblemen. He needed not the pomp and circumstance of heraldry to emblazon his name. . . . He was physically educated. Every muscle was developed, every nerve braced up, and his whole frame energized by manual labor. There had been, and probably is now, in some branch of the family, a coin or medal struck in England, on one side of which there is a muscular arm wielding a sledge. A significant symbol! David Wilkinson nobly responded to it. . . . He was a man!"

- 6 -

ELI WHITNEY

1765 - 1825

FATHER OF MASS PRODUCTION

THE SON of a mechanically inclined farmer of Westborough, Massachusetts, Eli Whitney was born December 8, 1765. The twig followed the bend of the tree, for by Eli's twelfth birthday he was his father's right-hand man in the business of making hoe and ax blades.

Moreover, according to a later recollection of his sister Elizabeth, it was young Eli who, seeing the demand created by the Revolutionary War, encouraged his father to set up a forge to make nails.

Then right after the conflict Eli devised a way to convert his father's forge into a factory. By drawing nails into hatpins, he helped to popularize a new style. "Ladies no longer tied on their bonnets; they 'pind' them on with three long pins." At fifteen Eli Whitney was a manufacturer.

But, above all, the bright, self-taught lad yearned for a college education. To make that possible, he secured a position at nearby Leicester Academy at seven dollars a month and board. The bargain was that in exchange for being Headmaster Ebenezer Craft's private pupil, he would teach in the lower grades. For five years he prepared himself for college.

At twenty-three—many years older than most freshmen—Eli Whitney was admitted to Yale College. Then an overnight trip from Westborough, New Haven was the farthest the farm boy had ever been from home.

Upon Whitney's graduation in 1792, Phineas Miller, a fellow alumnus, got him a tutoring job. Near Savannah, Miller managed Mulberry Grove, a plantation which the state of Georgia gratefully had given to the late General Nathanael Greene, a hero of the Revolution. Whitney taught children living on a neighboring estate. Soon, however, depressed by his low wages, he considered taking up law as a profession.

It transpired that the tutor had Widow Catherine Greene to thank for putting him back on the track of his genius.

Its lands worked out, the South was in the grip of a serious depression. Great plantations and small farms alike were going to seed. If only a satisfactory cotton could be raised, the South might gain a new lease on life. For the whirring Hargreaves and Arkwright spindles of Britain cried out, "Cotton! Cotton! Give us cotton!"

Soon after his arrival in the South, Whitney heard the

worried planters discuss their problem at Widow
Greene's table. The South could raise only an inferior
cotton—to clean it of seeds seemed impossible. The few
ginning machines were unsatisfactory.

"Why don't you apply to our young friend, Mr. Whitney, here?" Catherine Greene asked one day. "He can
make anything!"

Whitney demurred. "Gentlemen, I don't think I ever
saw cotton or cotton seed in my life!"

But in a matter of days he quietly had made—with the
aid of wires from a birdcage supplied by one of Mrs.
Greene's daughters—a little model of a cotton gin. The
machine was so ingenious and promising that the alert
Miller agreed to back it for half the profits.

This spelled the end of Eli Whitney as a teacher. The
inventor returned to New Haven where he established
a little "factory." On March 14, 1794, President Washington signed Whitney's first cotton gin patent. The
firm of Miller & Whitney was in business.

The Whitney machine—which employed an entirely
new principle from existing unsatisfactory cotton gins—
made the inferior cotton of the South a merchantable
product. Almost overnight Whitney was world-famous.
The onetime farm boy came to know personally Washington and Jefferson and men of like stature. Doors of
the capital's officialdom were wide open to him.

But the partners made the mistake of trying to gin all
the cotton themselves. Georgia planters and farmers rose
up against Miller & Whitney's ginnery venture, its exclusive privilege or "monopoly," as they called it. Whit-

ney's perfected machines were costly. There was a loophole in the patent law. Everywhere the farmer-mechanics built cheap gins, infringing on the Whitney patent. In 1797, three hundred secret gins operated. Instead of the $100,000 annual business anticipated, the partners faced ruin.

Suddenly Whitney's dream of honor and fortune was dashed. What would happen to his factory?

Eli Whitney was not a Yankee for nothing. Ambitious, resourceful, ingenious, on May 1, 1798, he wrote to Secretary of the Treasury Wolcott, stating that, while forced to postpone his present business of "making the patent machines for cleansing cotton," he wished to keep employed the workmen and apprentices whom he had trained in working wood and metal. He proposed, therefore, to undertake the manufacture of "ten to fifteen thousand stand of arms.

"I am persuaded that machinery moved by water [power] . . . would greatly diminish the labor and greatly facilitate the manufacture of this article. Machines for forging, rolling, planing, boring, grinding, polishing, etc., may all be made use of to advantage."

It was a staggering proposal. Small arms—that is, in this case musket—production was complicated. A musket comprised many parts, virtually each of which was handmade. Yet the Yankee genius offered to make a colossal number by machine!

Only the fact that Whitney had become a national figure as an inventor—this together with the crisis of war with France hanging over the capital—could account for the eager response he received from Wolcott. "Knowing your skill as a mechanick, I had before spoken of you to the Secretary of War . . . . Come to Philadelphia [then the nation's capital] as soon as possible."

Twelve days after arriving in the capital, the inventor drove away carrying in his pocket a $134,000 contract to manufacture "ten thousand stand of arms, or muskets, with bayonets and ramrods, complete, fit for service."

Whitney toiled day and night to equip and set in operation a new two-story factory he erected outside New Haven. But altogether it took him two years to get it in real working order. And small wonder! Never had a factory like it been built before.

In government arsenals where handmade muskets were turned out one man fashioned locks, another carved stocks and another produced barrels. Whitney first separated the processes, such as planing, filing and drilling, which were necessary to musket making. Then he assigned groups of workers to each division of manufacture—an entirely new practice.

Whitney's entire factory was a single, huge machine.

Going further, Whitney designed planing, filing and drilling machines which required little mechanical skill to operate and greatly simplified the labor. He introduced drilling by templets or patterns, filing by jigs or guides and the milling of irregular forms. With these devices and processes every part of a model musket could be copied with precision, and all copies of any part would be exactly alike.

Thus the Yankee genius originated interchangeability of parts. And not only were guns produced by such methods superior to handmade muskets, but the cost of manufacture was smaller and the replacement of parts cheaper and quicker.

By devising such methods and machines, Eli Whitney originated the twin principles of modern production—the subdivision of labor and the standardization of parts. He is the father of mass production.

Whitney lived in a humble cottage near his mill with a widow and an old maid as his housekeeper and cook. He called himself a "lonely old bachelor." Yet sharing his roof were his apprentice boys—sometimes as many as nine—and Philos, Elihu and Eli Whitney Blake, sons of his widowed sister, Elizabeth Blake. Under his watchful eye and tender ministrations the Blake boys were brought up and educated.

But Whitney's "loneliness" was not to last. On January 6, 1817, when he was 51 years old, "Uncle Eli" married Henrietta, daughter of his old friend, Judge Pierpont E. Edwards of New Haven. After a while the erstwhile bachelor was occupied not merely with nephews and apprentices but also with three daughters and a son. By this time the Whitney Arms Company was flourishing. The manufacturer had won over or defeated his enemies —some of them in high places—who had sought to ruin him by forcing cancellation of his government contracts. He gave his nephews a share in the business.

The Whitney Arms Company became a noted training ground for mechanics. Apprentice "graduates" found employment in government arsenals or in private machine shops. In Eli Whitney's arms plant as in Samuel Slater's textile mills, which at this time also were blossoming in New England, the machine tool industry of the United States flourished.

Free from harassment at last, happy with his young family, suddenly Whitney was struck down by a lingering, incurable illness. He died January 8, 1825, in his fifty-ninth year.

Eli Whitney's mind and his hands had to be busy. Until the day of his death they were—he even invented an instrument to help the doctor relieve his pain.

The day before he died Whitney wrote a long codicil to his will to insure the continuity of his business. The management went to Philos and Eli Whitney Blake, who were to remain in control until Eli Whitney, Jr., a lad of only four years, could take over.

The son was to become almost as gifted and ambitious as his parent. For ninety years one of the foremost arms manufacturers, the Whitney Arms Company in 1888 sold out to the Winchester Repeating Arms Company.

Of how many men—be they emperors or presidents, statesmen or scientists—can it be said more truly than of Eli Whitney, "He influenced the course of history"?

Through his gin, cotton became king, and the Yankee inventor lived to see it raise the South from destitution to prosperity and power. The year of his death cotton exports, valued at $37,000,000, totaled more than all other exports combined. And Southern cotton was helping launch the American textile industry.

Because the effects of his cotton gin were sudden and spectacular, Eli Whitney is remembered chiefly as its inventor. But of far greater importance and of more lasting benefit to mankind is his less-known role as the father of mass production.

The general adoption of his manufacturing methods provided widespread employment in factories throughout the nation. And the factories brought forth an unending flow of better products within the range of everyone's pocketbook.

Mass production, sired by Whitney, put sewing and washing machines and countless other appliances into millions of homes to reduce drudgery. The magic of Whitney's methods converted the automobile from an expensive toy to a daily necessity.

Mass production, in short, raised the American standard of living to the highest plane ever reached by man. It endowed the United States with the industrial supremacy that serves as the cornerstone of our national security and world leadership.

No king or conqueror ever changed a nation or the world as did Eli Whitney—or more truly for the better!

- 7 -

NICHOLAS-LOUIS ROBERT

1761 - 1828

FATHER OF THE PAPER INDUSTRY

BORN IN PARIS, December 2, 1761, in a family of modest circumstances, Nicholas-Louis Robert was a highstrung child, frail and studious. Yet he developed an ardent and fiery temperament which led him to seek adventure. He proved to be a brave soldier in battle against the British during the American War for Independence.

His service over, for ten years Robert was an obscure clerk—known only as a hard worker and a tinkerer at inventions—in the renowned Parisian publishing firm of St. Leger Didot. Then he was transferred to the publisher's paper mill at Essonnes to act as a sort of personnel manager.

Essonnes, where Nicholas-Louis was destined to become the father of the paper industry, had been a paper manufacturing center for over four hundred years. But the history of the art was lost in antiquity, for men always have wished to record their deeds and desires. Prehistoric man, groping for expression before paper, first cut and printed crude symbols on the walls of caves. Then he used natural substances, such as leaves, bark and wood, and finally, processed materials, such as metal, brick, and parchment, for picture writing. Not until approximately four thousand years before Christ did the Egyptians utilize papyrus as a practical medium for writing. This "paper" was made by gumming together strips of the inner pellicles, or skins, of the papyrus plant.

But Ts'ai Lun in China invented the first true paper around A.D. 105. He steeped rags in water until they were reduced to a mass of isolated fibers. After thoroughly soaking the fibers in a vat of water, he dropped into the vat a screenlike mold which filled with the thick mass. Then he drained off the water and on the surface of the mold was a layer of fibers which, when dried, was a sheet of paper.

Chinese paper found its way to the West over the famous "silk route" through Asia to Persia. The secret of its making was not learned until A.D. 751, however, when the Arabs acquired it from Chinese prisoners after the Battle of the River Tharaz. From Samarkand the craft spread to Bagdad, to Damascus, to Egypt and Morocco. In their invasion of Spain the Moors carried papermaking with them and soon it spread throughout medieval Europe. And through the ages the process had changed little when Robert first observed it at Essones.

In Didot's plant the skilled worker dipped a flat, sieve-like mold of given size into a vat filled with macerated fibers suspended in water. He drew forth on the mold's porous surface a thin layer of matted fibers—a sheet of paper.

At that time all paper was handmade. The dimensions of the sheet were limited, first because a mold beyond a certain size could not be balanced evenly by one man and, secondly, simply to conserve paper because of its scarcity and high cost. As late as 1818 the British government would jail anyone found producing a newspaper or a sheet exceeding 22 by 32 inches.

Necessarily few newspapers and books were made—and very little writing paper. But this was not only because they cost so much, it also was because few people could read and write.

For their news most people had to be content with the reports of the town crier, who was the newscaster of the day. He tramped through the streets, pausing at intervals to shout the latest happenings, reading from a sheet or scroll he carried in his hand. Thus news traveled slowly and only the most important facts could be told.

Robert was in his early thirties when he began devising a papermaking machine.

With Didot's blessing and financial assistance he built a small model of his machine. It failed. The inventor was for giving up, but Didot wouldn't hear of that. Through succeeding failures Didot was the tenacious one, and Robert, more temperamental, the one easily discouraged.

Didot placed skilled mechanics at his employee's serv-

ice. Though satisfied with the principle he had evolved, Robert could not get the small models he constructed to work. Then Didot financed a larger model and success appeared to be at hand.

Robert's machine applied the same principle underlying hand operation. It formed the paper on a woven-wire mold which retained the matted fibers while allowing the superfluous water to drain off. Yet it was revolutionary. For the hand process limited the size of the sheet of paper to the dimensions of the mold, whereas Robert's woven-wire mesh was a continuous machine operation permitting paper to be made in an endless length! Only the width was limited—to the width of the mold.

At this point St. Leger Didot insisted that Robert patent his machine. He introduced him to the Minister of the Interior, and Robert formally applied for a patent September 9, 1798. Upon seeing the machine, a member of the important French Bureau of Arts and Trades declared, "Citizen Robert is the first to imagine a machine capable of making paper from the vat. . . . From all reports it is an entirely new invention and deserves every encouragement." The bureau assigned draftsmen to work with Robert at Essonnes, and the government awarded the aspiring inventor 3000 francs.

Encouraged from all sides, the jubilant young man redrew the plans and again set down a comprehensive description. On January 18, 1799, his patent was granted. Didot footed the bill, which came to 1562 francs.

Though still in an experimental stage, a model of Robert's machine was exhibited at the Paris Exposition of 1801. It caused a sensation. In less than one month the model produced a continuous band of paper—about six inches wide—long enough to encircle the earth. France exulted. Paris named a street after Robert, so recently the unknown man.

Intoxicated with the prospect of success, Robert lost his head and became demanding. Quick riches appealed to him. He would sell his patent to the highest bidder. Didot resisted, and the inventor had him hailed into court. But Robert failed in his efforts to sell to others and sold his invention to Didot, who made a partial payment for the rights and then sought the funds to develop them. At the time, however, business conditions were against him. Napoleon Bonaparte was running wild in Europe. France, surrounded by enemies, had little money except for military needs.

But Didot was far from defeated. Running the blockade, he smuggled Robert's model into England where he enlisted the aid of his brother-in-law, John Gamble. The latter formed a partnership with Henry and Sealy Fourdrinier, a celebrated firm of London stationers. After three years of toilsome and expensive experiments, however, Gamble withdrew. His resources exhausted, he assigned his patent rights and interests to the Fourdriniers, who saw a great future for the invention.

Backing the machine with their wealth, the Fourdriniers engaged Bryan Donkin, a brilliant young machinist, who made several basic improvements. Entirely workable, Robert's machine was nearing the point of practicability. Some of the Fourdrinier-built machines were thirty feet long and made paper fifty-four inches wide. Each of them had the capacity of six average hand-operated paper mills.

But still more money and still more time were needed to perfect the machine and, after expending £60,000, or about $300,000, in developing it, the Fourdriniers went bankrupt.

The brothers suffered a double blow. The paper-makers who employed hand-labor methods fancied ruin ahead if such a machine as the Fourdriniers' came into general use. So they had obtained the passage of a law stating that no extension of a patent could be granted except to an original inventor. Not being the original inventors, the Fourdriniers could not obtain patent extensions and, as bankrupts, they could not collect royalties under the patents they had controlled.

In France, meantime, Didot had not continued his payments to Robert and the latter brought suit. Though the original inventor won his case and recovered his patents, he was unable to obtain the financial support necessary to complete the development of his machine. Robert, then, never got more than a pittance for his brilliant and original idea. He tried his hand at several other inventions—a "writing machine," a lithograph "copying machine," a "journal press," a sort of "multi-graphing machine"—but all were failures.

Twenty-five years after Didot had run the blockade with the plans, Robert's revolutionary papermaking machine came back to France labeled as a Fourdrinier and developed by English skill. Meantime, Robert, low in funds and discouraged, was long without work. In 1815, in order to support his wife and two children, he resorted to teaching in a primary school at Dreux. His children died when still young, and the sensitive teacher indulged his spare time writing poetry and composing music. But he did try one last invention—a pantograph for copying music on a stone lithograph. In 1828, at the age of sixty-seven, Robert died in obscurity, a poor and broken man.

And though the Fourdriniers lived to see the machine that bore their name make good their early claims, the brothers died in extreme poverty—Henry, in 1855, at the age of ninety.

So reads the sad story of the pioneers who gave the papermaking machine to the world. One and all, they failed to secure financial reward.

Even Robert's role might have been lost to posterity had not the descendants of Didot staged a celebration, a hundred years later, at the Paris Exposition. This celebration was to honor Robert on the occasion of the centennial of the first showing of his papermaking machine. Then many long-lost records were revealed.

Today the name of Nicholas-Louis Robert is cherished by papermakers the world over. To him must go the credit for originating the now indispensable machine that furnishes the paper of "an indefinite length" employed in printing all modern newspapers, magazines, books—in fact, practically all paper that is consumed. Thanks to it, paper is one of the most commonly used substances in modern living. Indeed, the machine "invented to throw people out of work" has built one of the greatest modern enterprises—the paper industry, which gives employment to millions throughout the world.

And in providing us with a plentiful and cheap material upon which to print and write, Robert, Didot, Gamble, the Fourdriniers and Donkin helped to make reading and writing—probably man's greatest gifts—the possession of the many instead of just the few.

What greater tribute could be paid than this to their genius and steadfastness—to their sincere efforts to develop a material upon which could be chronicled the history of man and the news of his day-to-day achievements?

8

JOHN LOUDON McADAM

1756 - 1836

FATHER OF MODERN ROADS

"Do NOT make the traffic to suit the roads, make the roads to suit the traffic." When, over a hundred and fifty years ago, John Loudon McAdam voiced this advice, England was in a turmoil over its highways. Road problems—or, on a broader basis, those of communication—have a way of always being with us. And with good reason. Possibly nothing touches the daily lives, the very progress of peoples, more vitally than the wide interchange of ideas, goods and services.

Before the invention of wheels man traveled by footpaths or trails. With the coming of vehicles he built some roads, but the world was sparsely settled then, and the need for them was not urgent. For centuries scattered settlements clung to coast lines and navigable waterways. The seas, rivers and canals were the "highways" of the time.

The first road builders meriting the name were the conquering Romans. Stretches of the great stone networks which they built for their armies and merchants remain today. And some are used as the foundations of modern highways.

Following the fall of Rome, however, barbarian hordes overran the civilized world, and travel was perilous for centuries. Man practically stopped using the wheel that he had invented, allowed the Roman roads to become buried from disuse, and built no worth-while highways. Later, this era became known as the Dark Ages, a name directly opposed to the civilizing function of roads.

In the seventeenth century, with the reappearance of carriages and stagecoaches and the re-establishment of defined routes and regular coach schedules, civilization began to look up. Yet for another hundred years travelers cried out with one voice against the scandalous condition of the highways.

In England the situation was indeed serious. James Watt had made the steam engine practicable, and Richard Arkwright had sparked the factory system with his spinning water frame. The two inventions were turning England upside down. Around lone factories on sylvan streams thriving towns sprang into life. People moved from farms to cities. Agricultural products had to be transported in increasing volume and over greater distances. Manufactured goods—turned out at low cost in unheard-of volume—had to be shipped to ready markets. But the potential life of this Industrial Revolution was nearly choked off by the ruts and bogs of unspeakable roads.

The man who cleared the blocks in the arteries of the Industrial Revolution was John Loudon McAdam, the father of modern roads.

Little is known of John McAdam's childhood except that he was born September 21, 1756, at Ayr, Scotland, in a well-to-do family and built, as a hobby, a model road section when he was a boy. When he was fourteen his father died. He went to New York to enter the counting-house of his merchant uncle, William McAdam. John did not direct his talents to the gigantic road problems of America, because he did not cast his lot with the new nation.

William McAdam had been in the British forces which had come to America under the Scottish Lord Loudon, and his army connections turned out profitably for his nephew. Much Tory blood ran in Scottish veins, and, when the Revolution began, not only did young McAdam side with the king, but his uncle secured for him the appointment as a prize-agent for the Port of New York. Every captured vessel brought in and sold by British privateers and men-of-war gave a percentage to the young Scotsman.

During the seven years of the war John McAdam accumulated a fortune. Most of it he carried back to Scotland when, in 1783, he fled Manhattan with his American wife, Glorianna Nicoll, and the rest of the Tories.

At twenty-seven, with an estate at Sanhie, Ayshire, McAdam was a country gentleman, upon whom Britain soon bestowed the usual offices given to persons of wealth and social importance. He became a county magistrate and deputy lord lieutenant as well as district road trustee. In the last-named office his boyhood hobby of scientific road building quickly ripened into a lifelong obsession.

The fact that public funds for road experiments were not available did not stop McAdam, and in furthering his research he cast aside his Scottish thrift. Using liberal amounts of his own money, he launched a one-man campaign, preaching the new and startling belief that Britain could prosper only by building and maintaining adequate roads. Over some ten years he traveled thirty thousand miles through Scotland and England, studying the highways that were the subject of his crusade and the object of his condemnation. He suffered ridicule and abuse, but increasingly his doctrine attracted attention.

As a result of his travels McAdam brought to public

attention an array of sorry facts. Ignorance as to what constituted good roads was profound and widespread. Stupidity and graft ruled Britain's road system under which each parish maintained its own roads. The "through highways" of the day were turnpikes, subject to toll, and they were owned by landed proprietors and managed by incompetent men. The entire system cried aloud for efficient and capable guidance.

McAdam's road building experiments and methods, as district road trustee, attracted wide attention.

McAdam was interested more in the repair and maintenance of old roads than in the construction of new ones. The main disadvantage of the typical road of the period, he found, was not so much that its surface was destroyed by the movement of traffic as that it was pushed out of place. All roads then were surfaced with round stones which shifted easily when the dirt and clay that bound them were loosened by rain or frost. McAdam knew that if he could contrive a surface that would stand up to traffic and weather he would solve the problem.

Proper drainage was a cardinal principle of McAdam's roadbuilding methods, and he used angular instead of round stones for a surface. Indeed, he demanded that stones be broken into pieces which could pass through an iron ring two and a half inches in diameter. When rolled, these angular pieces became firmly wedged against each other and so held together without a binding agent. Moreover, they formed a fast, hard surface resistant to rain and moisture. Disregarding a foundation for his roads, McAdam believed that any subsoil would carry any weight if it were properly drained and imperviously covered.

Contemporary with McAdam—and to an extent a rival—was Thomas B. Telford, a famed English civil engineer and canal and bridge builder, who gained high repute by building roads in remote areas of England and Scotland. Telford, too, insisted on good drainage and used carefully prepared surface materials, but his pitched foundation was diametrically opposed to Mc-Adam's method and was better applied to new than to old roads.

Not until 1816 did McAdam win official recognition. At fifty-one, he was made general surveyor of roads of the Bristol municipality with a £ 400-a-year salary, and for the first time he could conduct experiments not paid for out of his own pocket. Under McAdam's regime Bristol's roads, formerly known as "wikked wayes," became the talk of England as models of construction.

Reorganizing the road system from top to bottom, the Scot also excelled as an administrator. He dismissed the loafers who were supposed to maintain the king's highway and replaced them with skilled laborers. He created a new profession by training road builders in new construction and in methods of repair. He advocated that all district bodies should be controlled by a central administrative board responsible to the government. Envisioned by the father of modern roads, this body evolved into Britain's modern Ministry of Transport.

During McAdam's five years as Bristol's road supervisor his services came into great demand. Without charge he gave advice and assistance to seventy turnpike trusts—as the toll road companies were called— located in twenty-eight counties. His crusade was spreading.

But as recognition mounted so did opposition from the toll road interests and the incompetents and loafers in the county road system. The fiercer the battle grew, the harder the dour Scot fought back, completely ignoring his age and health. His three sons, who gave up lucrative positions to aid in spreading their father's system throughout Britain, ably bolstered his efforts.

After the publication in 1819 and 1820, respectively, of McAdam's two great treatises—*Scientific Repair* and *Preservation of Roads* and *The Present System of Road-Making*—a wave of public support turned the tide irrevocably in his favor.

"Yesterday the workmen began to Macadamize the wide roadway from Charing Cross to Parliament Street," noted the London *Times* of October 8, 1824. Not only was McAdam news, but his name, slightly changed in its spelling, had become a part of the English language!

McAdam's roads helped to launch Britain's great coach-travel era which lasted from 1820 into the 1840s. And macadamization unclogged the arteries of the Industrial Revolution. Hundreds of mail coaches and private carriages sped along the roads. Rumbling along more slowly, thousands of sturdy "waggons" facilitated the interchange of farm produce and factory products. Whole families were awheel. Taverns dotted roadsides, and the tourist trade boomed in every town. The coach era utilized some 150,000 horses and gave employment to 30,000 coachmen, guards and horsekeepers. Nothing like it occurred again until the coming of the Motor Age three quarters of a century later.

In presenting a silver pickax to McAdam on June 1, 1825, the street sweepers of the city of Huntington acknowledged his "giving permanent employment to hundreds." Twenty years later a London columnist who called himself "Nimrod" counted McAdam, next to Dr. Jenner of typhus fame, as "the greatest contributor to the welfare of mankind that this country has ever produced."

"Few people realize what McAdam did for his country," wrote C. M. Trevelyan in his *British History of the 19th Century*. "Had it not been for his roads the Industrial Revolution could not possibly have taken place, for there would have been no means of transport to the new markets that were indispensable to its increased production."

When McAdam took over the Bristol district in 1816, Great Britain had 700 miles of macadamized roads. At his death, twenty years later, only about 250 of the nation's 25,600 miles of high roads were not macadamized. And the Scottish road builder's methods had spread to many countries, including the rapidly expanding United States.

Not until 1827 did the sixty-two-year-old McAdam receive full recognition for his long crusade. Then the government made him General Surveyor of Roads of

Great Britain. A few years earlier the nation had granted him £2000 in reward for his services.

Some reports state that McAdam died a poor man, but these seem to be in error. Whether the government fully compensated him for his private outlays, as has been widely recorded, is not definitely established. But the fact remains that, after his second marriage at the age of seventy-one, he lived comfortably in Hertfordshire and mingled in the brilliant society of George IV's reign. He died November 26, 1836, at the age of eighty.

McAdam refused many rewards for his services, including an offer of knighthood, though his second son, Sir James Nicoll McAdam, who succeeded his father as General Surveyor of Roads, accepted the honor a year after his father's death.

At Moffat, Scotland, John Loudon McAdam rests in a cemetery surrounded by a romantic countryside dotted with ancient ruins, including the remains of Roman roads. Horse-drawn buggies jogged past his grave on macadamized roads until "gasoline buggies" compelled changes in road construction and materials.

When McAdam died the Railway Age was dawning, and iron rails, to an extent, supplanted roads. Again highways fell into neglect from disuse. For many years the belief was widespread that railways would eliminate the need for intercity and interregional roads. The Motor Age effectively shattered that idea.

Man's attainment of the motorcar represents an outstanding use of the wheel that he invented centuries ago, and his building of roads has always involved methods of using the wheel to the best advantage. Among those who have helped to develop those methods John Loudon McAdam stands as a forceful pioneer. His axiom, "Do not make the traffic to suit the roads, make the roads to suit the traffic," applies with even greater force today than it did in 1811 when first he stated it.

- 9 -

JOHN STEVENS

1749 - 1838

FATHER OF AMERICAN RAILROADS

IN ITS EARLY YEARS the United States was poor and weak. Inadequate and uncertain transportation isolated the few cities which clung to the Atlantic coast. George Washington's dream of a network of canals was slow to materialize. Roads scarcely existed. The relative ease of sea transportation made New York closer to Europe than to the Mississippi River.

Travelers journeyed by Concord coach, horseback or, preferably, by boat. Between New England towns they patronized the "Apple Tree Fleet" schooners whose skippers took bearings from orchards along the beaches. In winter a Philadelphian might travel by stagecoach to Baltimore in five days—with luck!

Pack-horse trains were common in the Appalachians. It took ten days for the news of Washington's death to reach Boston. Delegates often met difficulty and delay traveling to capitals for legislative sessions. Poor transportation hobbled the nation's economy and the functioning of its government. Unity was next to impossible.

Furthermore, beyond the Appalachians lay the challenge of a vast wilderness—almost trackless, largely unexplored and completely undeveloped.

During this period—considered as one of the most critical in America's history—Colonel John Stevens of New Jersey faced these challenges. Born in Manhattan and a graduate of King's College (now Columbia University), Stevens had been an officer in Washington's army. From 1777 to 1782 he had helped to finance the Revolution as treasurer of his state.

The ex-officer was deeply concerned with the progress of the new nation. America's greatest needs, he firmly believed, were self-sufficiency in engineering talent, materials and manufacturing. Adequate transportation he held to be its only escape from poverty and disunity. During a long and useful life he constantly preached and practiced his beliefs.

Stevens inherited large properties in New Jersey from his grandfather and father—each of whom had borne the name of John Stevens—and married Rachel Cox, the "belle of Bloomsbury," in that state. Two years later he bought a confiscated Tory estate, comprising the Hudson River island of Hoboken. Subsequently it was connected to the Jersey mainland by a causeway. With his island Stevens acquired the popular designation of "Colonel John of Hoboken" and an intense interest in

safe and speedy transportation across the Hudson to New York. Why not steam propulsion?

Like Benjamin Franklin and Thomas Jefferson, his contemporaries, Colonel John was a man of wide talents. By profession a lawyer, by inclination he was a mechanic and amateur engineer with the time and money to pursue his hobbies, which centered around steam.

In forges and machine shops, which he erected on his estate, in 1788 he built into a marine engine the first known multitubular steam boiler. To protect his invention he petitioned Congress for a patent law and outlined a suggested bill. When the legislators passed the Patent Law of 1790, Stevens became the father of our present patent system.

In 1802 Colonel John of Hoboken caused consternation among strollers in Manhattan's Battery Park by ferrying himself from his lower Broadway residence to his Hoboken estate in a puffing steamboat. His invention—which bobbed alarmingly on the choppy Hudson and sometimes "exploded"—came five years before Robert Fulton won a monopoly of river steam navigation with his paddle-wheeled *Clermont.*

Stevens' craft was the first steamboat with underwater screw-type propellors, and his later *Phoenix* became the first vessel to "steam" in ocean waters. Only by the proverbial eyelash did Colonel John Stevens of Hoboken lose to Fulton the honor of being the founder of the steamboat industry.

But Stevens' true interest lay in applying steam to land transportation. Pursuing that goal, he won greater distinction as the father of American railroads.

As early as 1790 Colonel John became convinced that railways would prove superior to canals in meeting America's colossal internal communication and transportation needs. In 1795—while George Stephenson, destined to become England's great locomotive and railroad builder, was still a lad helping his father in the

Wylam coal mines of Northumberland—Colonel John designed his first crude steam engine. Thereafter nothing could sway his belief that the country's future depended on developing steam railways. The purchase of the Louisiana Territory—which more than doubled the size of the United States and extended its bounds to the Pacific—added fervor to his argument.

Colonel John fought canals tooth and nail. In 1812, while opposing New York's Erie Canal, a pet project of Governor De Witt Clinton, Stevens submitted to the state legislature his *Documents Tending to Prove the Superior Advantages of Railways and Steam Carriers over Canal Navigation*. At the time the only "railroads" utilized wooden tracks and horse-drawn cars. Practical steam locomotives and railways did not exist. Yet, today, Stevens' pamphlet reads like a masterpiece of logic.

"So many and so important," he wrote, "are the advantages which these States would derive from the general adoption of the proposed steam railways, that they ought . . . to become an object of primary attention to the national government. . . . Two or three thousand dollars would . . . give the project a fair trial. On the success of this experiment, a plan should be digested, and the necessary surveys be made for the extension of these ways in all directions, so as to embrace and unite every section of this extensive empire. It might then . . . be truly said that these States would constitute one family, intimately connected . . . in bonds of indissoluble union."

Taking his case to cities and state legislatures, Stevens urged a railway between Philadelphia and Pittsburgh to open a market for farmers between the Delaware and Ohio rivers, or, as he put it, "to admit products from the West being profitably brought to the East." Canal advocates he declared to be "grasping at a shadow. . . . The present moment is critical." To objections about the mountain barrier he answered, "A railroad would scale the Alleghany or any other mountain, provided the grade were made low enough per mile."

When New York canal and turnpike interests turned heavy guns on Stevens, he counterfired explosively, "Long before . . . New York could accomplish so gigantic an enterprise [as completing its canals] the government could carry railroads into every section of the Union and thus . . . eclipse the state's premature, if not abortive, efforts. . . . Are the mouths of the Mississippi and the Hudson to remain forever the only outlets . . . for the Western States? I answer, NO!"

With some reason Steven's proposals met wide ridicule. Talk of equipping the nation with railroads was "like selling the skin of a bear before catching him." Where were the locomotives and rails? The necessary shops and mechanical talent?

Colonel John blazed the trail in 1825 by designing, building and operating a small self-propelled steam engine. Circling a track on his Hoboken estate, it became one of the wonders of the New World—nearby residents flocked to see it, and few travelers omitted it from their journeys. Thus Stevens captured public interest and gained disciples.

Though his Camden and Amboy Railroad was the first

railway to be charted in America (1815 by the state of New Jersey), not until 1830 could Colonel John find financial backing for it. Other ventures were more fortunate. The South Carolina Canal and Railway Company, the Mohawk and Hudson, the Baltimore and Ohio, the Delaware and Hudson, all predated Stevens' road with small stretches of track. Scarcely, however, did they compare with the Stockton and Darlington or the Liverpool and Manchester in Great Britain.

On the Stockton and Darlington, September 27, 1825, George Stephenson had launched the Railway Age with his locomotive *Active,* which hauled thirty-four tiny cars with a total load of ninety tons. Then his *Rocket* had won the Rainhill Trials, and he had begun the Liverpool and Manchester, a prodigious enterprise costing £800,-000. Opened to the public September 15, 1830, it has been called "the father and mother of all railroads, one of the peaks among the landmarks of man's history."

The Stevenses and the Stephensons were not strangers. Of the dozen children borne by Colonel John's wife, two sons—Robert Livingston and Edwin Augustus —followed their father's roadbed with great distinction. George Stephenson had a worthy colleague and successor in his only son Robert.

First contact between the two families came in 1830, when Robert Livingston Stevens went to England to order the *John Bull,* built to his specifications, at the Stephenson Locomotive Works. On this trip Robert designed the T-Rail, or "Stevens-Rail." Later came his hook-headed spike, his balance valve, his fishtail rail joint and other inventions and methods which became standard for most railroads.

Using his father's stone-block rail bed plan, as developed by his brother Edwin, Robert Stevens successfully tested the imported *John Bull* in September 1831, to fill his father's cup to overflowing. At eighty-two, Colonel John presided over a lawn party at Hoboken for two hundred distinguished guests "with spirits as abundant and sparkling as his champagne."

Though not the first British locomotive to be tried in America, the *John Bull* was the most successful up to that time. In 1854 Matthias Baldwin, founder of the famous locomotive works, patterned *Old Ironsides*, his first locomotive, after it. Soon American shops were turning out locomotives far more capable of pulling heavy loads, climbing steep grades and negotiating sharp curves than foreign makes.

In his latter years John Stevens turned to abstract studies, writing essays on metaphysics, economics, philosophy, politics and public education.

Both fathers—John Stevens and George Stephenson, self-taught engineers—saw that their sons received formal engineering training. Colonel John's sons and later descendants became noted engineers in their own right. Stephenson's son Robert attained such high honors in bridge design and construction that he was buried in Westminster Abbey.

And in September 1871 the Stevens Institute of Technology, built on the Hoboken estate, opened its doors to twenty-one students. In endowing the school Edwin fulfilled his father's dream that his country be provided with engineering talent. The institute created the first American degree in mechanical engineering.

"Railroad fever" was contagious in the United States. Before Colonel John died, March 6, 1838, at his Hoboken "Castle," railroads were fast overtaking canals in mileage. In the still young nation they spread and stimulated settlement, agriculture and industry. By 1869 steel rails linked the Atlantic and Pacific.

Colonel John's prophecy was realized. The railroads pointed the way, and millions of Americans and immigrants followed. Farms and cities sprouted and grew. The Iron Horse raced far ahead of canal and Concord coach. The romance of railroading stirred successive generations of American youths, and in developing the country railroads sounded bells and whistles, urgently calling for many materials. The steel and other industries stirred to thriving life.

A towering figure, Colonel John Stevens of Hoboken! America's railroads and their vital role in building and welding the nation—as he predicted and hastened—are a fitting monument to his convictions and energies!

Now, as the steam locomotive superseded coach and canal, so the Diesel-electric locomotive sends the puffing, shrilly neighing Iron Horse to pasture. At this development Colonel John—mighty advocate of steam—certainly would rejoice rather than turn in his grave.

For were he to see today's smokeless, cinderless, almost noiseless Diesel-electrics swiftly drawing streamlined trains of stainless steel or aluminum and long, heavy freights, the father of American railroads would simply point to one of his fundamental beliefs which he stated in 1806: "The wealth and prosperity of a nation may be said to depend almost entirely upon the facility and cheapness with which transportation is effected internally."

His was the *broad* vision.

- 10 -

ROBERT FULTON

1765 - 1815

FATHER OF MODERN MARINE TRANSPORTATION

IF EVER A MAN lived a storybook life, he was Robert Fulton. Born on a Pennsylvania farm in 1765, ten years before the American Revolution, he was the son of a Scotch-Irish immigrant tailor turned backwoodsman. But the backwoods boy lifted himself by his bootstraps to win recognition and splendor as the father of modern marine transportation.

Little is known of Fulton's early life. Mary, his mother, was widowed early, and to help support the large family Robert, clever with tools and machinery, was briefly apprenticed to a Philadelphia jeweler. There he began painting miniature portraits, thus gaining entré to wealthy families through whom he obtained letters of introduction to Benjamin West, the famous American painter in London.

When he was twenty-two the widow's son sailed for London with forty borrowed guineas and soon was living at the Wests'. Tall, handsome and graceful, with a vigorous mind and a ready tongue, his outstanding characteristic was ambition to succeed. He was made much of by the many artists, writers and scientists attracted to the Wests' salon. Yet four years of toiling at his art brought him small success, and, on his own again, he was close to starvation.

A failure? Fulton was not a man to admit defeat nor England a nation to reject the ambitious. The country was surcharged with the Industrial Revolution of Boulton & Watt's steam engine, of Arkwright's spinning

frame, of Maudslay's machine tools, of Lord Stanhope's canals—that is, with ideas. New engines and machines were bringing unheard-of prosperity. Canals and aqueducts were revolutionizing transportation and changing the face of the countryside. Realizing that success lay in another direction, Robert readily transferred his ability as an artist to specifications and blueprints and soon revealed marked talent for engineering.

He became interested in steamboats through the efforts of his friend James Rumsey and, after Rumsey's death in 1792, began painstaking experiments of his own on efficient paddle-wheel propulsion. But Fulton was quick to see that nobody was interested in steamboats —not even James Watt, father of the steam engine. England was canal mad.

So in 1794 the would-be engineer published a *Treatise on the Improvement of Canal Navigation*. His canals would be uniformly smaller and cheaper. Straight as arrows, they would have inclined planes instead of locks and "trains" of boats, a good deal like the railroad transportation system still to be invented! His book was crammed with meticulous drawings and intricate calculations. Persistently pressing his ideas, within a few years the audacious young American, who would discard prevailing canal practices, became one of the most discussed engineers of the day. But the British were so cold to his views that he moved to Paris. Ten years in England had won him only high standing as an engineer.

Fulton labored so hard to interest the French government in his canal system that he humorously wrote his mother, "And now . . . being unwed at the age of thirty-two years, the ladies of my acquaintance begin to fear that I shall die an old bachelor; hence with eyes full of regard and the sweetest arguments they persuade me to avoid such a miserable end."

Soon France and England were at war, and Fulton shifted his interest to submarines and torpedoes. With money raised by exhibiting his huge painting of Moscow in flames, he built a submarine and made successful dives with it in Brest Harbor. Called the *Nautilus,* its screw propeller was hand-operated by a crew of four. Courageously Fulton steered his frail craft for the mighty British fleet off Le Havre. But the warships had been forewarned and moved out of range.

Chancellor Robert R. Livingston of New York, who was visiting Paris to assist in negotiations with Napoleon for the purchase of Louisiana, became greatly impressed by Fulton's engineering ability. Livingston possessed an option from the New York Legislature on all steamboat navigation in the state. To hold his option, however, he needed a steamboat that would average at least four miles an hour between New York and Albany. Would Fulton build such a vessel and share equally, with Livingston, in an incorporated steamboat company? On October 10, 1802, the two signed a momentous agreement.

The young engineer built and tested his first steamboat—powered by a Boulton & Watt engine—on the Seine River, France, in 1803. The vessel sank. On the next trial, August 9, 1803, the rebuilt steamboat operated successfully. Its speed against the current, however, was only 2.9 miles per hour—too slow to win the New York monopoly.

Back in England, for three long, hard years Fulton devoted every spare minute to studying all known steamboat experiments. Finally, in August 1806, with perfected plans for a steamboat and a Boulton & Watt engine built to his exacting specifications, he sailed for America. When he stepped ashore in New York he had been abroad just short of twenty years. Always, however, he had shown pride in his American citizenship.

Busy as Fulton became, he now found time to fall in love and asked Chancellor Livingston, "Is it presumptuous in me to aspire to the hand of Miss Harriet Livingston?" On January 7, 1807, the former poor backwoods boy married his wealthy patron's niece.

The inventor set August 17, 1807, for a trial run of his craft. "Fulton's ingenious steamboat sails today from North Hudson River, near State Prison, to Albany," said the single newspaper that noticed the epochal event.

The "ingenious" vessel was the *Clermont*. Displacing 100 tons, she was a side-wheeler, 150 feet long, with an 18-foot beam and a 7-foot hold. Her mid-deck was crowded with a huge Boulton & Watt engine drive system, its piston 24 inches in diameter with a 4-foot stroke. Piles of cordwood fuel for the rectangular boiler, 8 feet wide by 20 feet long, were everywhere.

After one false start, the vessel steamed steadily up the scenic Hudson. Night fell, and for the first time the Catskills echoed to the panting of steam. Still the boat chugged on. Twenty-four hours after departing from New York, she anchored 110 miles upstream at Clermont-on-the-Hudson, Robert Livingston's vast estate, where the Chancellor welcomed Fulton and his adventurous passengers. In eight hours next day, the vessel covered the remaining 40 miles to Albany. The *Clermont's* 150-mile voyage in thirty-two hours had bettered the four-miles-per-hour requirement and secured the New York monopoly.

But why honor Robert Fulton's achievement? Why not honor instead John Fitch, James Rumsey, Oliver Evans, William Symington or the redoubtable Colonel John Stevens of Hoboken? All of them built and operated steamboats before the *Clermont*.

Fulton, however, followed through. Season after season the *Clermont* tirelessly plied her route. Diligently drumming up business, Livingston and Fulton cleared $16,000 in their first year of operation. In two more years the inventor enlarged his vessel, improved her engine and built two additional boats. With this *first steamship line,* Fulton launched modern marine transportation. For this achievement, and not for the invention of the first steamboat—a claim that he never made—Fulton is honored.

Each of Fulton's new steamboats was better than its predecessor. By 1815 he had built twenty-one and was the recognized leader of steam maritime construction.

His rewards were many. Profits poured in, and the once starving but always generous backwoods boy and painter became a gracious patron of the arts. Few were

the cultural or scientific societies of which he was not a
member.

When the War of 1812 threatened his country, Fulton
built the *Demologos,* the first steamship-of-war launched
by any nation. Finished too late to see combat, on October 29, 1814, she was formally christened *Fulton the
First* in a New York gay with flags, bunting and general
rejoicing. The inventor leaped to the stature of a national
hero. So great was his fame that authorities dared not
start the Erie Canal until he had favorably approved the
plans.

At the pinnacle of success, Fulton died suddenly on
February 23, 1815. Rarely has the nation so lamented
the passing of a private citizen. Shops closed. Members
of the New York Legislature and of numerous societies
wore mourning. Prominent leaders in government, business and society followed his bier as multitudes lined
the streets. Cannon boomed a slow cadence until the
procession entered Trinity Church where the tailor's son
was interred in the Livingston vault.

In one thirty-two-hour voyage, Fulton thrust mankind centuries ahead by tossing overboard primitive and
uncertain wind power. With dependable mechanical
propulsion an established fact, stern- or side-wheeled
boats multiplied rapidly on American rivers to play their
vital role in developing the new nation. Having patented
his invention in 1808, Fulton tried to gain monopolies
on all waterways. In 1823, however, the United States
Supreme Court subjected all rivers to federal jurisdic-
tion, thus opening them to competitive enterprise.

Soon steam vessels conquered the ocean and sped the benefits of world trade. But marine loads demanded more power, more speed and greater economy than had ever been asked of any machine. By mid-century screw-propelled steamships with expansion engines had arrived, and Fulton's invention was headed toward full-speed development.

Finding that a given amount of steam would do more work if it were first used in a high-pressure cylinder and then exhausted to a larger, low-pressure one, marine engine builders successively introduced the compound, the triple- and the quadruple-expansion power plants.

In the World War I era, many merchant and naval steam vessels substituted oil for coal fuel. The gains were numerous—savings in useful space, labor cost, fueling time and, more important, longer cruising ranges and greater speed. Then, slowly but surely, the more powerful and dependable oil-fueled Diesel engine displaced steam. Today it rules the waves.

Yet in 1955 the United States Navy introduced a new chapter in marine history with the first atomic-powered vessel, a submarine, fittingly christened the *Nautilus* in honor of Fulton's pioneering underwater craft. The possibilities of marine atomic power are vast. And they all stem back to the practical bent of Robert Fulton who, as one of America's first engineers, contributed much to the development of a continent and the progress of civilization.

- II -

CYRUS HALL McCORMICK

1809 - 1884

FATHER OF FARM MECHANIZATION

BORN THE ELDEST CHILD on the family farm, Walnut Grove, Rockland County, Virginia, February 15, 1809, Cyrus Hall McCormick, as a boy, preferred his father's log machine shop to farm work. This preference he inherited from his father, Robert. With a prosperous farm, with slaves for labor, with sawmills and gristmills humming, and with a distillery and a smelter bringing in revenue, Robert could indulge his mechanical bent. More than anything else in the world he wanted to give the world a grain reaper. Among young Cyrus' earliest recollections were his father's efforts at invention.

From the minute of his birth Cyrus McCormick was heir to another rich legacy. James Watt with his steam engine and Richard Arkwright with his spinning frame already had launched the Machine Age. And Eli Whitney with his cotton gin had proved that industry had no exclusive rights to mechanical tools and machines. The very age stimulated mathematical minds and adept hands to dream and labor at invention.

Whitney had crowned cotton king. Nevertheless, valuable as it was, the gin was useful in processing only one commodity. How much greater a reward in fame and fortune would fall to the inventor of a machine that would ease the centuries-long, backbreaking toil of the sickle and the scythe by harvesting all grain crops. Robert's dream must have touched Cyrus.

Like many others with the same idea, however, the McCormicks found that a workable reaper would be no simple gadget. To be successful the machine would have to operate on level and sloping land, over smooth and rough terrain. It would have to cut the grain, of course —and several attempted inventions had done that—but also it would have to lay down the grain in an untangled, reasonably straight row. Repeatedly, Robert McCormick attacked these problems, the last time in May 1831. Tragically, he failed.

Family legend says that Cyrus McCormick started his own experimenting with a reaper after his father's "final dismal failure" and accomplished in three months what his father had been unable to do in a lifetime! Eventually, even members of the McCormick family disputed the amount of originality that Cyrus had built into his reaper, so, possibly, the successful machine sprang from both father and son. Yet certain facts are clear.

In the following July under a hot sun, twenty-two-

year-old Cyrus demonstrated a reaper of his design. Drawn by a single horse between shafts, the machine had a reciprocating knife actuated by gears from a main wheel. Behind the cutter bar was a platform. On the outer end of the platform front was a pointed divider which separated the grain stalks for cutting. The cut stalks fell on the platform parallel to the horse. A man, walking behind, periodically raked the stalks from the platform in gavels, or bundles, ready for binding. Cyrus did not patent his reaper until 1834.

For ten years he diligently made and improved his reaper during the winter and energetically demonstrated it to farmers during the harvest season. His father aided him in his attempt to start a business. For Cyrus, they were ten years of toil and discouragements that might have broken another man. He had to ride for miles and days. He had to learn to give and watch credit.

But, with Cyrus McCormick, they were years which hardened a character of strong purpose and single-mindedness. He had set out to prove the worth of his invention. No stone would remain unturned to do so while energy responded. Possessed with the physique of a Hercules, which he had consciously developed at the forge in his father's blacksmith shop, there seemed no demands required in his travels, or in the long, taxing exertions of demonstrating his strange ware before skeptical farmers, too great for his inexhaustible endurance. He permitted himself no other interest. He had to meet the challenge of other reapers. Particularly of one patented by Obed Hussey of Ohio in December 1833, a little before McCormick's. As both inventors constantly improved their implements, bitter and prolonged would be the rivalry between the McCormick Patent Reaper and the Hussey machine manufactured in Baltimore.

By 1842 Cyrus had succeeded in selling only seven of his reapers. Small wonder, as one looks back at what they cost—$100 apiece, a tremendous investment for farmers at that time! But these sales were enough to finance Cyrus to increase his production and even to contract with certain other manufacturers to make his machines. Up to that time all McCormick reapers had been made at Walnut Grove. Then events occurred rapidly to change the picture. In 1846 Robert McCormick died. The mantle of head of the family fell on thirty-five-year-old Cyrus. With an authority that was to make him a somewhat awesome figure to his younger brothers and sisters for the rest of his life, he accepted his new responsibilities.

Already Cyrus had committed the McCormick family to the fate of his reaper. Not only had his father helped with the manufacture, but his brothers Leander and William were working for him. Moreover, he was ready to take the most important step in his life. In recent years he had extended his sales out from his native state and the East into the Middle West as far as Wisconsin. He had gazed upon the vast plain sweeping beyond the Mississippi. He had followed new railroads to their very westward termini. He had watched the detraining settlers. Some came from worn-out New England farms. Many were refugees from the famines which were sweeping Ireland and other European countries.

Had he envisioned these vast areas as fertile farm-lands? IIad he imagined the railroads branching out like nerve tentacles and activating new towns as they spread? In his mind's eye, had he seen the inflowing set-tlers as industrious and prosperous producers whose la-bor would feed a hungry world? All, given his reaper! He must have. For it was not in the conservative nature of the Scotch-Irish Cyrus McCormick to have taken the step he did, to tear up his family roots in the South, for the dubious prospects of the West, without a clear pic-ture of the probabilities.

In 1847 it took faith and imagination for McCormick to select Chicago for the site of his factory. Chicago was a mudhole, a dismal swamp with not a single paved street. A city of 10,000 persons living in rickety, un-painted frame shacks, it was still to have its first rail-road. But McCormick saw Chicago as a future railroad hub.

It took capital, too, which McCormick lacked and had to borrow. He found men who would help him, among them William B. Ogden, Chicago pioneer, railway builder and financial wizard. Cyrus installed Leander as head of manufacturing, William as head bookkeeper. Within two years, the creditors were repaid and Mc-Cormick & Company—much later the International Har-vester Company—was a sensational success.

Between 1848 and 1860 Cyrus McCormick engaged in numerous lawsuits against competitors, not always suc-cessfully, but always lustily. Probably his greatest battle

was to convince Congress that he should have an extension of his patent. He lost. But no legal or legislative
setback daunted him. Because of the excellence of his
machine, his energetic, original and aggressive business
methods, he gained an early lead in the opening farm-
lands of the West. Although the Hussey and other reapers, old and new, stayed actively in the field and grew
with this new revolution—the mechanization of the farm
—he left his competitors far behind.

For Cyrus Hall McCormick, in selling his reaper,
changed the farmer from a skeptic to a convert. When
he was not fighting a court battle or appearing before a
congressional committee, he was demonstrating his
reaper at state and county fairs, receiving callers, and
engaging in a mountain of business correspondence. His
letters, housed in the McCormick Historical Library at
the University of Wisconsin, make one of the fullest
records of American business development ever preserved.

In Chicago, Cyrus McCormick chose well and, in him,
Chicago gained another vigorous pioneer. Chicago's rise
as the grain center of the nation is the story of the rise
of Cyrus Hall McCormick and his reaper. In 1856 his
five-story factory, with a daily producing capacity of 40
reapers, actually turned out 4000 machines. Standing
on the Chicago River, the plant was one of the city's
largest and employed nearly 300 workers. Scarcely a
local newspaper in the wheat belt did not carry McCormick Patent Virginia Reaper ads. McCormick stood behind his machine with a guaranty "or your money back."
His ads featured farmers' testimonials. He granted long-

term credit to farmers. He was easy on them in drought years, helping them hang onto their land. His implement salesmen became part and parcel of the opening of the prairie states. By that time, too, McCormick was invading the foreign markets with his reaper.

By 1857, Cyrus McCormick was one of Chicago's and the nation's wealthiest and most influential men. Although he was a leader in community and church life and a recognized political power, his first preoccupation was with business. He visited and entertained celebrated persons. A handsome six-footer, weighing two hundred pounds, with dark, full beard, piercing brown eyes and a "fresh complexion," he was "a lion of a man in any company."

Yet by nature he was aloof. Many regarded him as cold. In certain respects he appeared to be unchanged from the man who twenty years before had ridden horseback over the Virginia mountains peddling his reaper, except that now he rode the trains. He had never married. His legal business had taken him much to Washington; his financial affairs and the promotion of his foreign business to New York. He lived in trains or hotels or in boarding houses in new Western towns. Much of his business he conducted in his hotel bedroom, bargaining while he shaved.

In September 1857 he met and fell in love with the young and charming Nancy Fowler, of Clayton, New York, whom he married January 26, 1858. Nor did this event immediately alter his traveling habits, his wife accompanying him and joyously aiding his secretaries in copying his endless correspondence. Even when the children came—by 1874 Nancy was the mother of five— her interest in his business continued. She was his constant companion.

The great Chicago fire of 1871 destroyed the McCormick plant. Cyrus was sixty-two and rich. "I at once determined to proceed with the work of rebuilding," he later told his grandson. His plant employed 700 workers. He felt an obligation to them and to the farmers. That year he made 10,000 reapers. His attitude was that of other Chicagoans, with whom he cooperated. Two years after the fire they opened a huge exposition building "to show the world that Chicago had come back."

Early in 1879 a brownstone mansion "decorated with carved paneling and the art of Europe" gave the McCormicks their "first home." Here the restless Cyrus finally settled. Five years later, May 13, 1884, there he "came to rest."

Cyrus McCormick did more than invent a machine and create a great business. He helped to settle the "breadbasket of the world" and aided in building our second largest city into a vital manufacturing, railroad and shipping center.

Moreover, McCormick's story is the story of the birth of the farm implement industry which made the United States one of the world's great agricultural nations. And the story tells of decreased farm drudgery, of greater profits for the farmer-entrepreneur, of abundant bread and food, of raising America's health and living standards.

For Cyrus Hall McCormick was the father of power

farming and the modern mechanized farm. His reaper replaced the sickle, the scythe and substituted the horse for man's muscle. Then the self-rake reaper, the harvester, the wire binder and the twine binder followed. Today the combine—the harvester-thresher—is the spectacular instrument of power farming, and tractors do the plowing and general utility work. Gasoline, kerosene and Diesel power are the sinews of the modern American farm. The revolution began with the reaper.

With mechanical power for sowing, cultivating and harvesting, farmers were able to work more land and produce more food with less physical effort. The coming of the automobile and better roads allowed them to truck products between farm and market, thus introducing a great transportation system which has bettered the whole aspect of farm economics and life.

McCormick died a millionaire. But his biographers say, he measured success only in accomplishment. Proudly he wore in his coat lapel the ribbon of the French Legion of Honor, awarded him in 1878 by the French Academy for "having done more for the cause of agriculture than any living man."

Thus Cyrus Hall McCormick ranks with Richard Arkwright, father of the Industrial Revolution. But farm mechanization, the revolution that McCormick started, is still in its infancy. Like the Industrial Revolution, it promises to be a powerful force for higher living standards throughout the world.

- 12 -

GAIL BORDEN

1801 - 1874

FATHER OF THE MODERN DAIRY INDUSTRY

WHEN HE PERFECTED his process for condensing milk, Gail Borden had never heard of germs. Yet his discovery was the rewarding result of a years-long search for pure food. Goaded by the sight of children dying aboard an immigrant ship because of drinking milk from infected cows, he was fifty-two when he began the experiments which were to make him father of the modern dairy industry.

"Gail Borden, son of Gail Borden and Philadelphia Wheeler Borden, November 9, 1801, Norwich, New York"—thus his mother inscribed his birth at the top of the children's column in the family Bible. When the lad was only fourteen, his parents packed their household goods and, with Gail and his three brothers, transferred their farming efforts first to Kentucky and then to Indiana. Sensitive, eager, determined, deeply religious, tall, handsome, rawboned, frail—all these words have been used to describe Gail Borden, who became the popular surveyor of Jefferson County, Indiana, when he was only twenty years old.

Yet from his early youth Gail had grown increasingly aware of the prevalence of sickness and death. Plagued by a persistent hacking cough, he finally sought a warmer climate to improve his health. He spent six and a half years in Amite County, Mississippi, surveying in summer and teaching school the year round. This life so restored his health that on September 28, 1828, he married Penelope Mercer, sixteen-year-old daughter of Colonel Eli Mercer.

In the following year, at New Orleans, the couple eagerly awaited the arrival of Gail's parents and his younger brothers. Previously Gail's next youngest brother, Tom, had migrated to Texas. At Tom's urging, the entire family had resolved to follow him. En route to the rendezvous, however, Gail's mother died at Memphis. Sorrowfully, the father and his sons boarded a steamer for Galveston.

In the history of the Lone Star State, the Borden name is prominent. Gail settled on his homestead of 4428 acres —a Spanish league—hopefully planning to try his hand at farming and cattle raising. Almost immediately, however, Stephen Austin, the founder of Texas, called him to San Felipe and plunged him into the thick of the Texas struggle for Mexican statehood and, finally, for independence from Mexico.

At first in charge of the vitally important land office, after the conflict broke Gail became publisher of the *Telegraph and Texas Register,* a newspaper which was to play an important part in rallying recruits to the Lone Star standard. In his paper Gail headlined Colonel Sydney Sherman's historic words, "Remember the Alamo!" helping make them the battle cry that inspired the new republic. As the enemy closed in, Gail sent his family to Galveston. Though the Mexicans burned his printshop and threw his presses into the river, the newspaperman carried on until, under Sam Houston, Texas won its freedom. Borden never forgot these seven years of high adventure, and to him Texas was always home.

President Houston made Gail the Collector of the Port of Galveston. The title was high-sounding and important, but not lucrative. Something more had to be done to support Penelope and his six children. Borden gave increased attention to an idea he had long nurtured—that food could be preserved and made safer by condensation. An intensely religious man of puritanical bent, he firmly believed that in trying to protect mankind against the frequent, life-snuffing diseases and epidemics of the time he would be serving his God. In 1844 Penelope and a four-year-old son died in a yellow fever epidemic that raged through Galveston. Thereafter Borden's concentration on his work grew almost to religious fervor. Two years later he lost another son.

Borden first experimented with meat. He made his product by boiling 120 pounds of beef down to 10, that is, by dehydrating and condensing it. Then he mixed flour with the extract, kneaded the substance into biscuits and baked them. A party of Forty-Niners took his biscuits to California during the gold rush, and Dr. Elisha Kent Kane used some on one of his arctic expeditions. Shortly thereafter the biscuits were recommended to the American Association for the Advancement of Science, and Gail and his brother Tom built a plant to produce them in Galveston.

In 1851 Gail climaxed five years of intensive development and promotion at the International Exhibition in London, where his product won awards and he gained honorary membership in the London Society of Arts. Triumphant, he imagined a wide use for his concentrated food by armies, navies, merchant vessels, hospitals and explorers.

Nevertheless, his five years of toiling at experiments and demonstrations ended in complete failure. Throughout the period he had lived from hand to mouth. During his long stays in Washington, New York and London, friends and neighbors had cared for his children. Creditors had hounded him. In 1852 he lost all that had gone into the Texas plant. Yet he wrote to a friend, "Don't infer I have given up, for I know that the meat biscuit is one of the discoveries of the age."

Years elapsed, however, before Borden returned to his meat biscuits. For, while returning from England, he had seen four or five distraught immigrant mothers holding dying infants in their arms as the result of impure milk from two infected cows carried aboard the steamer. The picture haunted him.

Milk, he knew, had been a major means of sustenance since animal life had come upon earth. But, he also knew, any natural milk might become contaminated even as infants, weaned from their mothers' breasts, cried for it. The problem was not new, for in that day before artificial refrigeration, chemists had often investigated the ease with which milk contaminated.

First, they noted the high water content of milk—about 87.34 per cent. Remove the water and the problem of milk's bulk, which vitally affected its transportation, would be solved. But how to remove the water without disturbing the taste of the solids? How, simultaneously, to make the concentrated milk keep better than the natural product?

Only two years after witnessing the heartbreaking deaths aboard the steamer, Borden found the answer that had long baffled the scientists. In 1853 he applied for a patent on a condensing process "to prevent the incipient decomposition of milk." He boiled off the water in milk in an airtight vacuum pan similar to those he had seen the Shakers of New Lebanon, New York, use when they condensed preserved sugar, fruit juices and extracts. From beginning to end, his process excluded air. The resulting product kept well for a long time. Jubilant, he wrote to a friend, "I have succeeded in concentrating milk 80 per cent . . . should I live two years I shall present the world an invention of vast import . . . Remember what I say. I will be recognized as the inventor of a great process."

Yet Borden encountered difficulty and delay when the patent commissioner could see nothing from which he could "conclude that this exclusion of air is important." The desperate inventor employed two noted American scientists who painstakingly checked every known attempt to condense milk and concluded that the use of the vacuum pan to keep out air was not only new but also important. On August 19, 1856, he got his patent.

Though he had won his three-year fight with the patent office, securing needed finances was difficult. He opened a plant at Wolcottville, Connecticut, but his backers became discouraged. Again his debts piled up, and constantly he had to seek new help. Not infrequently it was forthcoming. As one who aided him put it, "Mr. Borden was a man who carried a letter of credit in his face."

A prophetic statement. During a train trip to New York from his Connecticut factory, Gail Borden and a total stranger engaged in casual conversation. By the end of the journey his chance acquaintance, Jeremiah Milbank, a banker and wholesale grocer of New York, had agreed to pay all of Borden's debts for a share in the business. Moving his plant to Burrville, Connecticut, on May 11, 1857, the inventor founded the New York Condensed Milk Company, later to become the Borden Company. Borden continued his research and development work, while Milbank managed finances. The team was successful, but the company, and the entire budding condensed milk industry, hoed a hard row until the Civil War. Then the huge armies in the field created a demand for the new, easily transported, concentrated milk that, after Appomattox, spread to cities and towns and grew immensely with the years.

Gail Borden's prediction came true. He presented the world with an invention of great import. How epochal his discovery was in the advancement of health he and the scientists who backed his patent claims did not learn until after 1864. In that year Louis Pasteur, one of mankind's greatest benefactors, told the world of the nature and behavior of the microscopic organisms which came to be called "germs." Then Borden learned why his sweetened condensed milk remained wholesome and usable for long periods of time. The heat used in his process was sufficient to destroy the recognized milk-borne germs. The amount of sugar added preserved the milk by inhibiting the activity of germs.

That condensed milk became a wholesome sustaining food for generations of babies was Gail Borden's greatest satisfaction. The fortune resulting from his great discovery never diverted him from the obligation he felt to humanity. This devotion was the foundation of the modern dairy industry, for when Borden discovered that condensed milk was safe he determined to keep it so.

Long before he heard of Pasteur he had insisted on buying milk only from farmers who kept their barns and cattle clean. In hundreds of personal demonstrations he taught dairymen how to care for their cows and the milk they produced. Later, a number of his suggestions were incorporated into a "Dairyman's Ten Commandments" which formed the basis of many modern health department regulations. In a day when careless farming was the rule, Gail Borden initiated the high standards that prevail today.

Moreover, Borden's discovery increased the sale of dairy products and built public confidence in them. Before the use of his process, people used only a small portion of the dairy products available. Milk, butter and cheese usually were sold only within a few miles from where they were produced. Much of the milk, mainly a child's food, was never marketed.

Borden made it a food for anyone, anywhere. Starting with selling condensed milk in a pushcart during the winter, he leveled out the seasonal imbalance of milk production—usually a spring surplus and a winter short supply—by making milk available the year round. Today, thousands of distributors supply milk the year round, and the "milkman" has become an American institution. Also, Borden's condensed milk spearheaded an array of special products. Soon evaporated milk, ice cream, cheeses and milk powders were expanding the farmer's market.

Today, milk is recognized as the most complete of all foods. In many forms and in large amounts, it is enjoyed by children and adults alike. Dairy products constitute a major portion of the average American diet and are shipped from rich production areas to contribute to health standards in all parts of the world.

Gail Borden's triumph came late in life. At the close of the Civil War he was sixty-four. Increasingly he began turning over operation of the company to his sons, John and Henry Lee. By 1870 he was nearing the allotted threescore years and ten, and ready to retire. First he visited Woodlawn Cemetery, just north of Manhattan, and selected his burial site. There, on a shady knoll overlooking most of the cemetery, he had a huge granite milk can placed, instructing that it be removed at his burial. We can pardon the pride he felt in the reward that perseverance had brought him.

Then, his health failing, in 1872 he returned "home" to Texas. Idleness bored him. The great failure of his life—the meat biscuit—gnawed at his memory. "Don't infer that I have given up," he had declared. He built a small meat-preserving plant and put Henry Lee in charge. The little town that grew up around the plant carried the name of Borden, Texas. There Gail Borden lived and worked until his death on January 11, 1874, at the age of seventy-two.

Soon after, his instructions were carried out at Woodlawn Cemetery, and the milk can was replaced by a monument. Its simple epitaph reads, "I tried and failed, I tried again and again, and succeeded."

- 13 -

CHARLES GOODYEAR

1800 - 1860

FATHER OF THE RUBBER INDUSTRY

CHARLES GOODYEAR, father of the rubber industry, was well acquainted with hardship and suffering. Even when he received a distinguished award for discovering the vulcanization of rubber, he was confined in a debtors' jail.

Often called crazy, Goodyear heard his ability questioned and his revolutionary invention termed "pure accident." Frequently he advertised and exploited his discovery with circus-like methods, for he was not overly modest. Basically, however, he was dedicated to research and entirely unconcerned with life's routine. His outbursts of exultation and display were sporadic, and because of bad luck or instability—fate, if you will—he was periodically imprisoned for debt.

The inventor's first acquaintance with debtors' prison

—a survival of medieval times which Charles Dickens soon was to help to oblivion—came at the age of thirty. Born at New Haven, Connecticut, December 29, 1800, Goodyear grew into a slender, delicate lad who aspired to the ministry. At twenty-one, however, he became a partner with his father, Amasa, in one of America's early hardware manufacturing ventures. The 1830 depression brought failure, and Charles, shouldering the firm's debts, was hustled off to his first jail term. Marital status and parenthood notwithstanding—ultimately he and Clarissa, his wife, had five children—Goodyear was to serve several such terms. Philosophically, he utilized the periods to study chemistry.

Goodyear's interest in finding a method of making India rubber capable of withstanding temperature extremes began in 1832, when, without scientific training, he tried to improve the rubberized clothing, shoes and life preservers made by the Roxbury Rubber Company, Roxbury, Connecticut. The rubber products of that day became brittle in cold and gummy under heat. By treating rubber with sulphuric acid, he attained seeming success in correcting this problem. In 1836 he hired a plant on Staten Island, opened a salesroom on nearby Broadway and secured a government contract to manufacture mailbags. His project collapsed when he found his rubber fabric to be useless under high temperatures.

Goodyear then worked with Nathaniel Hayward, a former employee of the Roxbury Rubber firm, who also was experimenting with sulphur and rubber. No success resulted, and the uncertain breadwinner wandered from town to town with Clarissa and their increasing brood. Living in desolate quarters, they were destitute, ill nourished and sickly. Often Charles actually begged for food. Finally William DeForrest, Goodyear's brother-in-law, took them into his Woburn, Massachusetts, home.

There, in 1839, on a day believed to have been February 23, the shivering family huddled close to the kitchen stove. Dull-eyed and miserable, they almost ignored the shabby Charles—looking older than his thirty-eight years—intently fiddling with his endless and noxious experiments. But his daughter saw a sudden glow of triumph spread over his face. Accidentally, he had dropped some India rubber mixed with sulphur on the red-hot stove.

A different version of the incident is that Clarissa—in a flare of rebellion against constant sacrifice—had forbidden Charles to pursue his experiments. Nevertheless, he secretly continued them. Upon her unexpected return from a visit, he tried to rid himself of the potion in the stove, spilling it on the hot lid. This version is unconfirmed.

His daughter, recalling her father's "look of exultation," continued: "He nailed the gum outside in the intense cold. Next morning . . . it was perfectly flexible. . . ."

Goodyear and others had tried to "tan" or "cure" rubber—as leather was treated—to make it impervious to heat and cold. But on the stove his mixture had hardened rather than melted. Was it possible that a certain degree of high temperature would cancel out the effect of heat itself? He experimented along this line and nearly two years later filed a caveat of intention. He applied for a patent July 7, 1843, and June 14, 1844, it was granted.

In his two-volume autobiography—liberally flavored with rubber sales promotion and published by himself in 1853/5—Goodyear noted, "I was surprised . . . that a specimen [in] contact with a hot stove charred like leather. . . . If the charring . . . could be stopped at the right moment, it might [lose] its stickiness. . . . Upon further ·trials . . . I was convinced that my inference was sound."

The mark of the inventor's genius was his pursuit of this clue, for the application of heat to rubber was the reverse of existent scientific knowledge. Was his discovery accidental? Goodyear admitted "that [my] discoveries were not the result of scientific . . . investigation," but claimed that they evolved from "the closest application and observation" rather than accident.

Application and observation at terrible sacrifice! For ten years Goodyear had persisted, had seen "those dear to him . . . stripped of comforts . . . everything they possessed brought under the hammer." He had been driven to "the forlorn resort of the . . . pawnbroker's shop," and he had not hesitated to sell even his children's schoolbooks. "The *certainty* of success warranted the measure which in other circumstances would have been sacrilege."

And during that epochal yet terrible winter, while in Boston in a fruitless effort to get backers, he was jailed for failure to pay his five-dollar hotel bill. When released, he trudged fifteen miles to Woburn and found his infant son William dying.

Sometimes miracles happen. DeForrest and others financed the inventor's new process. Henry, Nelson and Charles, Jr.—far more practical than their father—operated factories at Naugatuck, Connecticut. By 1841 money was rolling in, and the inventor paid his staggering debts totaling $35,000. But, ever the incorrigible researcher, he was far more interested in finding proven uses for rubber than in money. He sold licenses and manufacturing rights at ridiculously low figures. Constantly beset with infringements, he remained convinced that the golden flood would never end.

In 1851 Goodyear staged a sensational $30,000 Vulcanite Court at the Crystal Palace International Exhibition in London. The display failed to establish his claims over those of a Briton named Thomas Hancock and thus win the right to open factories in England. For the same case in America, however, Goodyear retained Daniel Webster at a $25,000 fee and won a clean-cut victory. He had "persisted and finally succeeded" where others had failed, said the court.

The inventor's 1855 venture in France was as unfortunate as his English experience. At the Paris Exhibition his process received the Gold Medal. Emperor Louis Napoleon acclaimed him as the greatest American since Franklin and named him for the Cross of the Legion of

Honor. But Goodyear's income from license fees could not match his $50,000 exhibition expense. Though ailing and on crutches, he was committed to the infamous Clichy jail.

There, in an unheated cell, his son Charles pinned on his father's breast the Legion of Honor medal. Friends soon secured the inventor's release.

In the quest of his goal Charles Goodyear spared neither himself nor those dearest to him. Overwork, hunger, broken health mattered not. He truly grieved at dragging his family through dire poverty, but, to him, the end he sought justified every sacrifice, and attainment always seemed close at hand. India rubber, or gum-elastic as he called it, was his obsession. If he had been an artist, rubber would have been his art; if a philosopher, his thesis; if a preacher, his cause.

For in Goodyear's mind materialistic progress undoubtedly was tinged with a spiritual meaning. His daily world was comfortless, inconvenient and wasteful. Society yearned for the materialistic advantages which we enjoy and which, oddly enough, some of us think it fashionable to deride. But it was a world wakening from a long sleep through the magic of discovery and invention, and Goodyear's attitude toward rubber reveals a fuller understanding of the blessings of materialistic progress.

Speaking of himself in the third person, the inventor wrote, "The creature may imagine he is only executing some plan of his own, while he is the instrument in the hands of his Maker . . . to execute His purposes which, though we cannot fathom, we may believe, involve with the highest elevation of mind and morals, the . . . improvement of things material. . . .

"Independent of . . . pecuniary considerations, he [Goodyear] has taken great satisfaction in trying to improve articles . . . for the use of man. . . . Imperfections of these things . . . he considered as of great importance . . . not only the cause of much waste of time and money, but also productive of great moral evil. . . .

"In any case it has been necessity . . . and moral as well as pecuniary obligations, with the ambition of making these inventions worthy of this age of improvements, that has stimulated the inventor to proceed, step by step, to the completion of his plan."

Knowing that Goodyear once seriously considered entering the ministry, one sees clearly that he was possessed with the concentration, fervor and faith of a zealot. Money and fame meant nothing. His sole interest was achievement in the interests of progress and humanity. The discovery of vulcanization only spurred him to greater effort in his chosen medium of rubber. Not satisfied to settle on one rubber product and make a fortune, Goodyear, like a great artist, used his profits to "buy more paint," ever experimenting with and making new products. In 1853 he listed hundreds of uses for rubber under every conceivable heading.

Toward the end of his days the inventor's inattention to the realities of his manufacturing enterprise became alarming, and even his long-suffering family finally became annoyed with his obsession to *prove* that the uses of rubber were unlimited. By 1860 he was feeble, but in June he made a business trip to Washington. While there he received a message to hasten to New Haven where his daughter had become critically ill. He never reached his destination. On July 1 he was carried ashore from a coastal vessel at New York. Upon learning that his daughter had died, "he folded his tired hands and went to sleep."

Though widely thought to be worth millions, Goodyear died $200,000 in debt. Four years later Charles, Jr., petitioned Congress to extend his father's patent rights so that the surviving family might profit. In recognition of the inventor's lifetime of struggle and of his heavy liabilities—all incurred for the "creation of [the] very improvements which have greatly enriched the world within these five years, and which must . . . still further . . . add untold millions to the wealth of man"— the request was granted.

Even Goodyear's vivid imagination did not foresee the extent to which posterity would vindicate his dream of thousands of rubber uses. Exhaustive as his ideas were, one searches vainly for mention of the rubber tire. Who in 1860—the day of ironbound carriage and wagon wheels—could have foreseen the rubber-tired "horseless carriage"?

Could he return today, Charles Goodyear would see himself, because of his invention of vulcanization, hailed by all rubber companies as the father of the industry. He would see that one company, with which he and his family were never connected, was named in his honor.

He would delight in the millions of motorcars smoothly rolling on rubber. But he would be puzzled to find materialistic progress—as he understood it—the object of criticism. His satisfaction would lie in the reality that one of the greatest benefits to society—rubber—had been realized.

- 14 -

SIR HENRY BESSEMER

1813 - 1898

FATHER OF THE STEEL INDUSTRY

THOUGH SOME STEEL was made years before his birth and others shared in bringing his process to success, Sir Henry Bessemer may be said to be overwhelmingly the father of the steel industry. Indeed Bessemer was an overwhelming man.

Energetic, curious and ingenious, his accomplishments in invention were amazing. His feats sometimes were fantastic, but, successes or failures, all were on a grand scale. Yet his instinct for financial advancement was keen and sure.

When he turned his talents to steelmaking and came up with the process that gave progress to the world and distinction to his name, Bessemer already was a wealthy, well-known British inventor. His interests sprang from a stimulating background.

Henry was born on January 19, 1813, on a small landed estate, Charlton House, in Hertfordshire, England, belonging to his artist-inventor father, Anthony, a refugee from the French Revolution. Anthony Bessemer, a member of France's Academy of Sciences, had found refuge and employment in London. From cutting letter punches in Henry Caslon's famous type foundry he had progressed to such skill that he set up his own type foundry on the grounds at Charlton House—a favorite haunt of the boy, Henry, who early showed a flair for invention.

After leaving school, "I begged my father to let me

remain home and learn something of practical engineering," Bessemer related in his *Autobiography*. His father agreed—indeed bought him "one of those beautiful small slide-rest lathes . . . and after a year or two at vise and lathe and other practical mechanical work, my father allowed me to employ myself making models of the too-numerous schemes which the vivid imagination of youth suggested."

At seventeen, a fraction over six feet tall and "well endowed with youthful energy" and "of an extremely sanguine temperament," Henry went off to London to seek his fortune. Meeting an Italian seller of penny plaster casts, he tried his hand on the "reproduction in metal of natural objects, both vegetable and mineral." Soon he was besieging British Museum officials to accept his work. He got a cold turndown.

He produced a fine bust of Shakespeare, using a wax process of his own invention that would give sculptors a casting in one piece instead of a dozen pieces which had to be fitted together.

Then he "achieved what was in reality my first concreat work." He produced dies suitable for stamping ornamental scrollwork. Henry's decorative stampings appeared on the covers of thousands of Bibles that went into British homes.

But when he came upon a distinctly different way of making dies which were capable of reproducing thousands of facsimile impressions, he really thought his fortune was made. At the time stamp forgeries had the government badly worried. He took a packet of stamps he had reproduced to Sir Charles Presley, head of the Stamp Office. "How do you know they're forged?" asked the official, squinting through a magnifying glass.

"Because I forged them myself!"

The Stamp Office merely adopted one of Bessemer's plates "as a security against forgery." It was a bitter pill. Henry, now all of nineteen, had counted on being "handsomely rewarded" so that "I might establish myself in a new home and marry the young lady to whom I have for two years been engaged."

He never forgot this incident. Forty-six years later—in 1878—the now world-famous inventor of the Bessemer steel process wrote a letter to the London *Times*. He belabored the government for its shabby treatment of a young inventor who had "no friends at court" and mused on "The Reward of Invention," as he titled his piece. The letter created a sensation. Henry Bessemer's long-remembered irritation was eased when, the following year, he knelt before Queen Victoria and was knighted.

Undaunted, young Bessemer fared better with a "gold dust" machine than with his stamp-reproducing device. One day he analyzed some bronze powder his sister used to make "gold" color for her painting on wood and china. Finding its excessive cost was due to its being hand-ground, he invented a machine which produced the powder at a fraction of its former cost. He kept the machine and its operation a closely guarded secret.

Henry was made. Money rolled in. He married his young lady and indulged a childhood dream—to have his own estate like Charlton House and upon it set up his shops and conduct his experiments. To his newly acquired Baxter House in the quiet London suburb of St. Pancras he moved his bride and some of her relatives to whom he entrusted the manufacture of gold dust. The secret of his process was kept for forty years—until he turned the business over to his brother-in-law as a reward for long and closemouthed service.

At Baxter House, Bessemer tried his hand at many experiments. Though ignorant of metallurgy, he knew that the times demanded cheaper and stronger iron. He experimented intensively for two years. The result of his labor was a large furnace, mounted on trunnions so that it could be rotated, with a perforated bottom through which air might be blown—to become famous as the Bessemer converter.

At last, he was ready. He started the blast of air and had half a ton of molten pig iron poured in. Oxygen in the air kept the mass burning so that no fuel was needed. With a tremendous roar a volcano-like torrent of sparks erupted. The cover of the furnace melted. Then quickly the tempest died. In a matter of minutes Bessemer had made in his converter ductile iron that would have required hours of work by one puddler. Better still, he had made steel in unheard-of quantity!

Telling of his reaction to his discovery, the inventor writes: "I had now incontrovertible evidence of the all-important fact that molten pig iron could, without the employment of any combustible matter, except that which it contained, be raised in the space of half an hour to a temperature previously unknown in the manufacturing arts, while it was simultaneously deprived of its carbon and silicon, wholly without skilled manipulation.

"What all this meant, what a perfect revolution it threatened in every iron-making district in the world, was fully grasped by the mind as I gazed motionless on the glowing ingot, the mere contemplation of which almost overwhelmed me for the time, notwithstanding that I had for weeks looked forward to that moment with a full knowledge that it meant an immense success, or a crushing failure of all my hopes and aspirations.

"I soon, however, felt a strong desire to test the quality of the metal, but I had no appliances to hammer or roll such a formidable mass; indeed, we had no means to hand even to move it. But I saw that there was one proof possible to which I could subject the ingot where it stood, and calling for an ordinary carpenter's axe, I dealt it three severe blows on the sharp angle of the prism.

"The cutting edge of the axe penetrated far into the soft metal, bulging the piece forward but not separating it. Had it been cast iron those angle-pieces would have been scattered all over the place in red-hot fragments, but their standing firm and undetachable assured me that the metal was malleable."

Bessemer first patented his "manufacture of malleable iron and steel without fuel" on October 15, 1855. He officially announced his discovery the next year at the Cheltenham meeting of the British Association for the Advancement of Science.

But as sometimes happens in invention, independently and unknown to each other, two men with an ocean between them had conceived the same principle of making steel. William Kelly, organizer of a company owning two iron furnaces and 14,000 acres of land in Kentucky, had begun his experiments in 1847—seven years before Bessemer's in England. He had succeeded in refining iron by subjecting it to a blast of air in a specially constructed furnace.

However, Kelly did not apply for a patent until 1857, two years after Bessemer's patent was granted. Though his invention was not wholly successful, Kelly was a prosperous ironmaster when the Bessemer process was introduced to America. Many river steamboats of the day had boilers made of plates produced at Kelly's plant.

In this country, because of patent litigation, neither the Kelly interests nor the Bessemer group could make much progress until the two were merged.

More fortunate than some pioneer inventors, Bessemer reaped a full harvest in return for his ingenuity and perseverance. For his sons he built the famous Sheffield Works and became a leading steelmaker. In royalties for making steel under his patents he received well over $5,000,000.

Bessemer steel might have failed at the start and certainly would not have progressed as far as it did but for two men. One was the Englishman, Robert Mushet, who righted a fault in Bessemer's process by introducing spiegeleisen—a variety of pig iron containing up to fifteen or twenty per cent of manganese—to steelmaking. The other was the American, A. L. Holley, colorful former New York journalist. In 1862, on behalf of a syndicate known as the "Bessemer Association," Holley purchased Bessemer's American patents and widely introduced the process in the United States. Actually many of the notable improvements in the so-called Bessemer method were made in American plants during the eighteen years intervening before Holley's death.

And production soared. In 1868 Bessemer steel output in the United States totaled only 8500 net tons against Britain's 110,000 gross tons. Eleven years later the two nations turned out equal quantities. Then the United States took the lead in a runaway race based on steel rails that carried settlers westward and built new and bigger cities. In 1902 we produced 9,138,000 gross tons against Germany's 5,230,000, Britain's 1,826,000 and France's 1,000,000 tons. Soon—in 1908—Bessemer steel production yielded first honors to open-hearth steel. Today in the United States, open-hearth furnaces account for ninety-one per cent of all the steel made.

But one of Bessemer's greatest prides was the fact that several American towns were named in his honor. And it can be truly said that, as America made steel, steel made America.

First at Baxter House, then at his Highgate estate, which he called Charlton after his boyhood home, and later at Denmark Hall, to which he retired in 1872, Bessemer never ceased experimenting. Knighted in 1879, a recipient of honors from many countries, he went on with his inventions.

Some were fantastic, perhaps. For instance, his channel boat with a luxurious "suspended" cabin to offset the roll and pitch of the sea that came to grief against the ferry piles at Calais and bankrupted the Bessemer Saloon Ship Company. Or perhaps the experimental telescope he installed in a large observatory on the grounds of Denmark Hall. Or his giant solar furnace.

But Bessemer, inventor to the last, believed in all of his experiments to the end—even including his novel channel boat.

He died on March 15, 1898, only a few months after losing his bride of sixty-three years.

Of Bessemer's 120 patents, the specifications filling nine bulky volumes, only one was great. But that—his process for making steel—was eminently great. For in one limitless leap steel carried the world from its centuries-old arduous and imperfect "iron age" to an age approaching perfection in metals. Bessemer's converters substituted science and precision for muscle and sweat in the rapid, large-scale production of steel.

Nothing advanced the Machine Age, with all of its physical benefits and cultural advantages, more than steel. And in the vast fields of agriculture, manufacturing, transportation, construction and communication— "wherever there is enterprise"—this basic material is to be found in ever increasing quantities.

The vision that Sir Henry Bessemer saw in his hour of triumph, when the first half ton of iron was poured into his first converter, has been more than fulfilled. The industry has rapidly grown and expanded, ever developing better products in ample volume to meet the needs of the nation in war and in peace. Indeed the steel industry truly inherited its founder's motto in life: "Onward ever!"

- 15 -

EDWIN L. DRAKE

1819 - 1880

FATHER OF THE PETROLEUM INDUSTRY

GEORGE H. BISSELL, a struggling young lawyer, while walking down New York's Broadway one summer day in 1857, was attracted to the window of an apothecary's shop by an imitation greenback advertising Samuel M. Kier's "Petroleum or Rock Oil, Celebrated for Its Wonderful Curative Powers."

The drawings next to the lettering held Bissell's eye. They showed derricks used in boring and pumping Kier's salt brine wells—the "rock oil" or petroleum being simply a by-product which the resourceful Kier was trying to get rid of.

Bissell had the flash of an idea. He became absorbed in those salt well derricks. His interest was not because he saw himself founding an industry that would convert a smelly liquid into products among the most useful

ever known to mankind. No, Bissell was just a private citizen with his eyes open and his senses alert to the opportunities afforded by private enterprise.

Three years before Bissell had become an oil man of sorts purely by accident. In 1854, while visiting his alma mater, Dartmouth College, he saw there a sample of the latest laboratory curiosity—a bottle of "rock oil"—which a chemistry professor friend told him might yield a kind of coal-oil illuminant. About a decade before, a process had been invented to convert coal into oil, and coal oil, or kerosene, was a novelty. However, illumination of that period was largely supplied by the tallow candle and whale oil.

Learning where the sample came from, Bissell persuaded his former law partner, Jonathan G. Eveleth, to join him in a new venture. They bought, in November 1854, part of the farm of the Brewer, Watson Lumber Company on Oil Creek, in remote western Pennsylvania, near Titusville.

The partners' first move was to have the land trenched to collect seepage oil, the first three barrels of which they sent for analysis to the distinguished Benjamin Silliman, Jr., professor of chemistry at Yale University.

Bissell and Eveleth then formed the Pennsylvania Rock Oil Company that same year, 1854. It was the first petroleum company ever organized. By the time Silliman's report was ready, in April 1855, the partners were so short of funds that Silliman held up the document until they paid his $526.08 bill in advance.

Silliman summed up his analysis in these words: "In

short, your company have in their possession a raw material from which, by simple and not expensive process, they may manufacture very valuable products."

But there things had stood, with nothing being done, and installments coming due with embarrassing regularity on the Oil Creek land purchase. And three years had passed! All they had gotten was a niggardly few barrels of oil by trenching the seepages and dipping out the liquid in buckets or wringing it out of saturated blankets. Something had to be done to save their investment.

Obviously one thing long uppermost in Bissell's mind was: "Beneath the ground there must be a pool of oil from which this seepage oil comes; how can we get that oil up to the surface?" As he stood under the awning of the apothecary's shop, he found himself with the answer —the derricks at Samuel Kier's salt plant at Tarentum, depicted on the imitation greenback. Why not develop petroleum by boring and pumping just as salt properties were operated?

There it was! No one had thought of it before—or if anyone had, no one had tried it. Petroleum, held prisoner in the earth for centuries, was to be released at last!

But Bissell's idea apparently didn't set the stockholders of the Pennsylvania Rock Oil Company on fire. The project languished. The panic of 1857 overwhelmed the partners. A group of New Haven stockholders, headed by James M. Townsend, president of the City Savings Bank of New Haven, took over. Bissell and Eveleth retained only a royalty interest.

Townsend lived at the Tontine Hotel in New Haven. Boarding at the hotel at the time was Edwin Laurentine Drake, thirty-eight, a widower of a year, and his small son. Because of a temporary illness, Drake had left his conductor's job on the New York & New Haven Railroad. Townsend knew Drake as a jack-of-all-trades who had been brought up on New York and Vermont farms and worked as hotel clerk and freight agent before becoming a conductor.

He knew, too, that Drake still possessed his railroad pass. He would bolster up Drake's spirit by suggesting that he look over the property, which Drake could reach at no transportation cost to the thrifty Townsend. Drake agreed to go. To impress people he was to see, Townsend sent letters ahead of Drake's arrival addressed to "Colonel" E. L. Drake.

Townsend then reorganized the Pennsylvania Rock Oil Company and changed the name to the Seneca Oil Company. Outraged protests from Bissell and Eveleth! Drake was made general manager at an annual salary of $1000, and given an additional $1000 to begin drilling for oil on the Titusville land. In May 1858 Drake moved his son and new wife to the American Hotel at Titusville, a little lumber town in the Pennsylvania wilderness.

Drake also brought along with him—if not experience —a Yankee resourcefulness and determination. Moreover, his constitution must have been rugged. It had to be for him to endure the severe climate, primitive conditions, and the hardships that were in store for him. He knew nothing about drilling a well. But he learned by visiting the salt operations at Tarentum. He proceeded cautiously. It was not until April of the next year that he decided how to proceed and had the man he wanted to help him—William A. (Uncle Billy) Smith, experienced salt well driller. Smith was assisted by his two young sons. They "rigged up" in June 1859.

The drilling site was in a remote, sparsely settled, heavily forested region on Oil Creek, with practically no transportation facilities. Where heretofore the Indian and the early settler had knelt beside the oil springs and blanket-wrung the oil to use on cuts and bruises, there stood a crude derrick. A walking beam caused a drill bit on a hemp rope to rise and fall and bury itself in the ground. The power was steam, generated in a curious old engine which filled the forest with its groans. At Titusville, an astonished citizenry discussed "Drakes Folly."

The sound of the drill was first heard in August 1859. Rock was struck at 36 feet. It was good hard rock, and if luck was with them, the drillers could do about three feet a day. But all sorts of difficulties were encountered.

On August 27, 1859, late on a Saturday afternoon, the drill dropped into a crevice. Uncle Billy Smith and his son Sam drew the iron bit from the well hole and stopped work for the day. On Sunday, as they began to lower a measuring rope into the 69½-foot-deep well, they encountered a black, oily fluid a few feet from the top of the hole. They had struck oil! Using a tin pitcher pump, they raised a quantity of the liquid. At sunset

Sam, with a sample of the oil, raced for Titusville.

Drake's Folly an oil well! Titusville went wild. The news was telegraphed to hamlets and cities far and wide, reaching a dynamic people who had just staged the California gold rush and were alert to every new opportunity.

Drake's well started a boom that rivaled, and had far greater significance than, the California gold rush. It was touched off by the lure of "liquid gold" on the one hand, and by the receptiveness of the world toward a universal illuminant on the other. If oil could be pumped out of wells like water, here was a source of light great enough to supply the needs of all, and money could be made developing it. Twenty-five barrels of oil a day were being pumped from the Drake well, and oil was selling at eighteen dollars a barrel! Here was unheard-of wealth for one lucky enough to strike oil!

The great flow of western migration had shunned western Pennsylvania as too rugged and unfriendly for settlement. Now, suddenly, a strip of this country not over fifty miles long was transformed into a great trade center, with towns elbowing one another for a place. Thousands upon thousands of people poured into the oil regions. Pithole City, a few miles from Titusville, within three months after the discovery of a well in its vicinity, grew from a few shacks to a city housing 20,-000, then 30,000 people.

On every farm, in every poor settlement of the region, there was some man ready to risk everything on drilling for oil, and bolstering him up soon after were the youths being discharged from the Union Army after the Civil War. They came from New York, Ohio, everywhere, to seek their fortunes in oil. Many wells were drilled immediately after the Drake well struck oil. Some were flowing wells, "gushers," producing 2000, 3000, or 4000 barrels a day.

But no longer was crude oil worth eighteen dollars a barrel. In January 1860 the price had dropped to ten dollars; by the close of 1861, to ten cents! Oil gushed out in floods; the world was ready for it, yes, but how was it to be saved, stored, transported, refined, and made available for use?

Seldom in history were men faced with greater problems than these oil pioneers. An abundant material, in itself valueless, poured forth upon them in a then remote part of the world—an inflammable liquid, that had to be transported like coal or grain, and had to be refined by processes still in the laboratory stage. In short, here was a product for which the world was crying, but for whose development no commercial machinery had yet been invented.

That this machinery came rapidly is proof of American initiative and resourcefulness. Reservoirs to receive the oil were excavated in the earth and lined with logs and cement, and boxlike structures of planks or logs. These gave way to huge wooden receptacles or tanks, holding hundreds of barrels.

After rail and barge lines had extended into the oil regions, great trains of oil-barrel-laden wagons on almost impassable roads were to be seen. The teamster era was to give way to the short iron pipe line, a unique invention for oil transportation. On the railroads, the first flatcards, laden with oil barrels, gave way to cars equipped with wooden tanks. These, in turn, stepped aside for steel tank cars.

Batteries of stills were erected in the oil regions, and some took on the aspect of sizable manufacturing plants. In Pittsburgh and New York, coal-oil plants became petroleum refineries.

Within a half dozen years of the drilling of the Drake well, oil refineries were making three grades of illuminating oil—"prime white," "standard white" and "straw white." Only a few years later they also were making lubricating oils.

Permanent tanks for carrying oil were placed in vessels—the birth of the tank ship.

Within ten years of the drilling of the Drake well, U.S. kerosene was going to the far corners of the earth. Soon the whaling fleets struck their flags as the world swiftly switched from the sperm-oil lamp to the kerosene lamp.

In almost a day, it seems—within no more than a dozen years in reality—there was a good steady light to read by, available to all the world—to promote safety, to facilitate education. No greater tribute than this could be paid to the energy, resourcefulness and courage of the men who founded one of America's greatest industries—the petroleum industry.

Who was the father of the petroleum industry? Bissell, who had the "great idea"? Drake, who made it work?

Townsend, who put up some of the needed money at a critical time? In a true sense, they all were, for together they supplied the essential ingredients of business achievement—ideas, labor and capital.

However, there wasn't a dissenting vote among the Pennsylvania pioneers when the question had a thorough airing in the sixties and early seventies. Drake was their man. Old-timers in Titusville recalled the agony of the drilling operation, the slurs they had cast on him. Drake's constant search for additional funds was successful only because of his standing in the community. In the words of their testimonial, "Edwin L. Drake was the man who first bored for oil, and by his genius and indomitable perseverance, produced the cheapest illuminator of the age, multiplying the wealth of the world, adding to the list of human industries, and contributing to the comfort and happiness of mankind."

When Bissell heard of Drake's discovery he hurried to Titusville. He leased much land for little or nothing because people were not yet aware of the value of the oil. He had luck in striking oil in several wells. He prospered, and continued as an executive of successful oil companies until his death in 1884.

Drake, on the other hand, "shook the boughs for others to gather the fruit." After drilling his well, he chose to become a justice of the peace in Titusville in 1860. He did a land-office business in witnessing legal conveyances during the rush. Three years later he left Titusville with $15,000 to become a broker specializing in oil securities in Wall Street.

But fortune was not kind to Drake. Ill-health overtook him and for years he could not work. He was confined to an invalid chair, with a neuralgic affliction of the spine. His wife attended him, kept house, cared for the children and took in sewing. An old Titusville friend met him in New York in 1869. Observing his invalid condition and learning that he had only sixty cents in his pocket, he staked him to twenty dollars. This friend took the news back to Titusville. A public subscription of $5000 was raised.

In 1873 persistent friends succeeded in having the Pennsylvania State Legislature pass a bill providing Drake with an annual income of $1500 during his life. Meantime the Drakes moved to South Bethlehem, Pennsylvania. Drake's end came only after seven more years of suffering—in November 1880.

Years later—October 4, 1901—a magnificent monument to his memory, and memorializing the Drake well, was erected in Woodlawn Cemetery at Titusville, and there Drake's body lies.

Today, at the site of this epochal event of August 27, 1859, stands the Drake Museum, a treasure house of oil industry mementos, which is visited by tourists from far and wide. There suitable ceremonies are conducted annually by an industry appreciative of its pioneers, whether successful or luckless.

Drake's contribution was vital and lasting, for the product which he first produced on a commercial basis has become firmly woven into the fabric of life throughout the world.

- 16 -

THOMAS A. EDISON

1847 - 1931

FATHER OF THE ELECTRICAL INDUSTRY

As AN INVETERATE INVENTOR, Thomas Edison won great successes and "fathered" more than one industry. But probably his greatest renown is as father of the electrical industry, a title which he himself never claimed. Better than any other person, Edison knew that no one man invented electricity or its thousand and one applications.

In his combined workshop and laboratory at Menlo Park and later at Orange—both in New Jersey—Edison worked on various inventions for more than fifty years. At sixty-one, he had taken out 1033 patents.

Heaven only knows how many he held when, after eighty-four years of life, he was laid to rest in 1931. A sorrowing nation mourned "America's greatest inventor," and people everywhere sorely missed the irascible, gentle, lovable and quotable hermit-inventor-philosopher.

For years he had been a prominent and productive figure and had contributed eloquently to the American way of life.

Thomas Alva Edison was born at Milan, Ohio, February 11, 1847, and spent his early years in Port Huron, Michigan. As a boy he simply could not be diverted from making chemical experiments. At twelve he left school and became a newsboy on the Grand Trunk Railway to finance his probings into unknown fields. Before he was fifteen he was proprietor of two stores—one selling periodicals, the other vegetables—and was hiring a newsboy for his train route.

These were the years of the Civil War. Recognizing a tremendous demand for newspapers as a result of the Battle of Shiloh, young Edison negotiated a loan from the editor of the Detroit *Free Press*, bought a thousand papers and sold them from the train at twenty-five cents apiece. Later, in a baggage car, he set up a small hand printing press, with which he published the *Weekly Herald* and sold over 400 copies a month. Inevitably, however, next to his press he operated a laboratory, and when a stick of phosphorous set fire to his chemicals, the editor-reporter-printer-news-agent summarily was dispossessed!

Edison's deafness may have dated from this mishap, but not from the fire or explosion. A well-meaning friend is said to have saved him from the boxcar-laboratory inferno by lifting him out by his ears. Another version of the story is that a railroad official soundly boxed his ears. Some people believed that the inventor's affliction en-

Menlo
Park

abled him to think better, to exclude outside distractions and avoid the waste of time listening to meaningless talk.

During the same year, 1862, Edison himself saved a life. From the path of a fast freight he snatched the baby son of station agent J. U. Mackenzie. As were all such employees in those days, Mackenzie was a telegrapher. In gratitude for the rescue he taught Edison train telegraphy.

Thus, when he was only sixteen, Tom was night operator at Stratford Junction, Ontario, on the Grand Trunk Railway, and soon he became a journeyman telegrapher for the Western Union Telegraph Company. Though one of the fastest operators, he was one of the most irritable. Too often his mind was teeming with thoughts of experiment and invention.

Moreover, his retiring manner, his utter disregard for his hair—though he was always smooth-shaven—his untidy dress, his brisk and unusual opinions, all made many people think him eccentric.

Wherever Thomas Edison lighted—Indianapolis, Cincinnati, Boston—he set up a workshop. While in the last-named city he took out his first patent—a vote-recording machine. Operated by electricity, the device allowed members of legislative bodies to register their names under the "ayes" or "noes" simply by moving a switch on their desks to right or left. A dial indicator, controlled by the same current, recorded the total vote.

Eager young Edison showed the machine to congressmen in Washington. It was too good! They didn't want anything that might speed up the long-drawn-out process of counting votes or interfere with filibustering. "Take it away!" they said.

But now Edison's mind was set. Despite everything he would be an inventor. He hounded crochety Dr. Norvin Green, president of the Western Union Telegraph Company, begging him to back his experiments. Constantly rebuffed, he decided to quit telegraphy, at least as an operator. It interfered too much with his experiments.

Edison went to New York. He had no money, for every cent he had made had gone for books or apparatus. Soon he found that without capital, he could make no headway as an inventor.

He applied for a job in Wall Street at the office of the Gold and Stock Indicator Company, makers of tickers—sensational new machines that delivered up-to-the-minute stock quotations to brokerage offices. While he was waiting, the central machine broke down and no one could repair it. Edison, the man of the hour, soon had it running, and the company employed him as manager of servicing at the fabulous salary of $3600 a year!

Immediately Edison opened a little workshop, set out his telegraph and electrical instruments and his bottles of chemicals. He bought more books, more batteries. And upon finishing his daily stint at the indicator company, he spent long hours—often the entire night—experimenting in his laboratory.

Hiring a clever mechanic named Callahan to help him, Edison invented important ticker improvements. General Marshal Lefferts, president of the indicator company, sent for him and gave him a check for $40,000 for his ticker patents. When the young inventor took the check to a bank, the teller refused to honor it. Until a friend straightened it all out by identifying him, Edison thought he had been "done."

Sudden riches gave new assurance to the inventor. Again he bearded Dr. Green, for he was certain that the Western Union Telegraph Company could best handle his inventions. He was convinced, too, that an inventor, engaged in the wide and varied fields which he wished to enter, would need the capital that only the resources of a large corporation could assure. Thus, before the day when companies had their own scientific research departments, Edison determined to supply the need himself.

This time Dr. Green became convinced and, with Western Union's co-operation, Edison opened a large shop and laboratory in Newark, New Jersey. While producing tickers, he experimented continually with telegraphic improvements. So, in 1870, at twenty-three Edison was a successful inventor and manufacturer.

Then, in rapid succession, Edison improved the printing telegraph and developed duplex and quadruplex telegraphy. Jay Gould purchased the rights to the last-named invention for $30,000

In 1876 the inventor moved to the little New Jersey town of Menlo Park, which was to gain lasting fame as the home of the Edison laboratory.

Here the inventor gathered around him a band of devoted young assistants whom, by his own example, he drove day and night. For many years his working schedule averaged more than eighteen hours a day.

In 1877 he applied for a patent for a "phonograph and speaking machine." This was a hand-operated model. Ten years later he developed a motor-driven one with cylindrical wax records. Later still he made records in the disk form which is still in use today.

Now Edison was off on a new course—electric lighting. He made innumerable experiments with all kinds of materials collected from all parts of the world. He worked with detail and care. He spent over $100,000, a tremendous sum for those days. The result was his discovery and development of the small, practical, incandescent electric lamp. Today, it lights the world.

Then, beginning on New Year's Eve, 1879, successive episodes of a dramatic serial story sprang from the inventor's brain. First, Edison displayed "light strung on wires" from his laboratory, an achievement in itself sufficient to excite the world. After almost to years of assembling and installing engines, dynamos, lamps, underground feeders and mains, switches, meters and sockets, the story reached its climax. On September 4, 1882, the Edison company turned on the current in its central lighting station at 257 Pearl Street, New York. The world gasped at the wonders of "The Wizard of Menlo Park."

So began the first regular distribution of electric light. The company had only 57 customers, all promised free current for three months. But, on a paying basis, only a month after the bonus period, Edison was lighting 5000 lamps in 225 homes, including J. Pierpont Morgan's.

Electric power transmission had arrived. This was Edison's great gift to the electrical industry, the contribution which entitles him to be honored as its founder.

Often Edison has been called America's greatest man of science. Yet he never qualified as a scientist in a formal college or university. He had no degree in chemistry and none in electrical engineering. He wasn't even a high school graduate. Only through his own efforts did he become a highly educated man. From his mother, who had been a schoolteacher, he learned the invaluable lesson of how to apply himself.

Numerous drawings exist of young Edison, with his head propped upon his arm and a solemn, dreamy look in his eyes. They are entirely imaginary and wrong. He was alert, indomitably determined and restlessly energetic. For fifty years his "trade mark" was a long linen duster—a "masculine Mother Hubbard," one admirer called it. Later in life he discarded the convenient garment, together with the inevitable, dilapidated straw hat, and began to take more care of his personal appearance.

An affectionate husband and father, Edison also made fast friends, notably with Harvey Firestone and Henry Ford. Often the three men vacationed together. Since he had ideas and was willing to put them into words or onto paper, the inventor was a joy to reporters the world over.

Edison's manufacturing enterprises became a vital part of the General Electric Company when it was organized in 1892. In Schenectady, in 1900, the company established a great research laboratory which attracted and developed many able scientists who, in turn, carried their assignments in electrical research to tremendous fulfillment.

For, as Edison had foreseen and demonstrated, technological advancement, or modern invention, depends on organization, on the accumulation and study of existing knowledge, on continuing experimentation and, above all, on the teamwork of devoted workers in the laboratory.

The industrial laboratory has vaster and much more readily available facilities than those of the lone inventor. Problems too difficult or too lengthy for one man to handle are solved more speedily when split into sub-problems and assigned to specialists.

Much of America's manufacturing "know-how" leans heavily on the laboratory's "find-how." In this field alone Edison made a major contribution toward building American living standards higher than those of any nation in world history.

The story of the research and engineering laboratories in every modern industry is the same. It is one of improving, perfecting and—not the least—creating new products and uses, which in turn create new industrial activity and more jobs.

Thomas Edison lived to see not merely buildings and streets illuminated by electricity. Before his death homes were equipped with electrically run washing machines, refrigerators, vacuum cleaners, stoves, toasters, sewing machines and scores of other convenient devices, all of which help to eliminate drudgery, lighten the load of daily life and improve the nation's health.

He lived to see man harness with electricity the power resources of steam, of the Diesel engine and of water— that vast source of power in nature. Within his time he saw all of these forces serving city dwellers, farmers, industrial plants, and various modes of transportation practically everywhere in the land. Perhaps he wanted no greater reward.

- 17 -

NIKOLAUS AUGUST OTTO

1832 - 1891

FATHER OF THE INTERNAL COMBUSTION ENGINE

ALMOST EVERYBODY knows about James Watt and his steam engine. Comparatively few people have ever heard of Nikolaus August Otto and his "gas" engine. Yet, what Watt was to the steam engine, Otto was to the internal combustion engine. Each man made practicable a prime mover of inestimable worth to the world.

The son of an innkeeper at Holzhausen on the Heather in Nassau, Germany, Nikolaus August was born June 14, 1832. He came late in his parents' lives. His father did not long survive. For many years Wilhelmina, a beloved older sister, operated the inn with her husband. Her attachment to her brother was more affectionate than dutiful and prevailed throughout her life.

After completing school with high marks and serving a three-year apprenticeship with a neighborhood merchant, Nikolaus left his peaceful town for bustling Cologne and became a salesman. He was almost thirty when he first became aware of gas engines. One such engine, built by J. J. E. Lenoir, French inventor, could scarcely escape his eye, for it was being widely advertised and exhibited in 1860.

Two years before, Nikolaus had become engaged to Anna Gossi. He was restless and ambitious. The much-touted gas engines, he thought, might be a promising line for an energetic salesman. That idea launched Otto into gas engine development—that and the hope he might gain the security necessary to wed Anna. Until that time he would remain a bachelor.

This type of engine had its beginnings in 1680 when Christian Huygens, a Dutch astronomer, sought a mechanical motive power to accomplish what man had done for centuries by sweat and muscle. At that time engines were unknown. But, taking his life in his hands, Huygens exploded a small amount of gunpowder in a cylinder closed by a piston. The piston moved!

Thus began experimentation for motive power by explosion, but soon—not surprisingly—gunpowder was dropped. From Huygens' until Lenoir's time, dozens of inventors strove to find the key. Some tried inflammable gas, others a mixture of vaporized spirits of turpentine and air, and still others a combination of air and illuminating gas. Their efforts were futile.

Meanwhile, Newcomen, Watt and others had succeeded with the steam engine. And the widely promoted Lenoir gas engine that had attracted Otto's attention

worked exactly like a double-acting steam engine of normal horizontal pattern. A substantial advance over any previously made gas engine, nevertheless Lenoir's engine was woefully extravagant in fuel consumption.

Otto was a commercial man. On his travels he had seen European cities and farms clamoring for efficient engines to keep apace of the spreading Industrial Revolution. He was convinced that the right gas engine could successfully compete with the cumbersome but all-conquering coal-fueled steam engines which by now were on every hand, even driving locomotives and ships. In 1861 he determined to invent the "right" one, to accept the challenge of his age. If only he could succeed! For Anna still waited.

The inventor's efforts bore quick fruit. During 1864, in partnership with Eugen Langen, an engineer possess-

ing financial resources, he founded N. A. Otto and Company. Two years later the firm patented Otto's vertical atmospheric engine, a material advance in the science of gas engines. Consuming two thirds less fuel than the Lenoir engine, Otto's invention stole the show at the

Paris Exhibition of 1867. Next year Anna and Nikolaus —after waiting ten years—could safely marry.

Encouraged by their success, the partners built a factory near Cologne at Deutz. Business was brisk. In 1872 Otto and Langen formed the firm destined to win world fame, first as the Gasmotorenfabrik Deutz—today known as Klöckner-Humboldt-Deutz, A.G. Here two engineers also destined for greatness received their early training —Gottlieb Daimler, inventor of a famous automobile, and William Maybach, builder of renowned motorcar and aircraft engines.

Though commercial success was his, Otto was still unsatisfied. The engine of his dream—one that could challenge steam—was not yet developed.

The earliest gas engines utilized a cycle similar to that in the steam engine, where the charge was fired all in the first or outstroke.

As early as 1862, even shortly before, Otto had run a motor experimentally on the four-stroke cycle. Unknown to him, this principle was proposed in 1862 by a Frenchman with the romantic name of Alphonse Beau de Rochas. It involved the following sequence of operations: (1) suction of fuel into the cylinder during the first outstroke of the piston; (2) compression of the mixture during the following instroke; (3) ignition of the compressed charge at the dead point and subsequent expulsion of the exploded gases during the next outstroke or "working stroke"; and (4) expulsion of the burned or expanded gases during the next instroke. But the principle existed in theory only.

Siegfried Marcus, an Austrian, invented a four-stroke cycle gas engine in 1873 which still is in possession of the Austrian Automobile Club. But, his experiments proving unsuccessful, he abandoned his efforts.

In 1876, after many years of unsparing day and night toil, Nikolaus Otto first successfully built the four-stroke cycle into an engine, calling it the Otto "silent" gas engine. However, the firm made the mistake of manufacturing and selling the engine before patenting it. A patent was not secured until August 4, 1877. Otto was now forty-five. Only fourteen years had elapsed since an ambitious drummer, fascinated by Lenoir's engine, had turned earnest inventor.

At the Paris Exhibition of 1878 the firm formally introduced its perfected Otto "silent" engine with sensational success. Before, gas engines had sounded like an artillery barrage. At last a practically soundless explosion engine! And with a gas consumption rate of 20 cubic feet per effective horsepower—as compared with 44 cubic feet in Otto's previous atmospheric engine and more than 100 cubic feet in the Lenoir engine—the "silent" engine offered unbelievable economy as well as greater efficiency!

The secret lay in the four-stroke principle, known ever since as the Otto-cycle. Commonplace today, it is familiar to everyone who has tinkered with an automobile engine.

Like many other pioneers, the company no sooner achieved success than it found itself in litigation. Choosing to represent the firm himself, Otto defended his claims in France and Germany during a strenuous ten-year battle that sapped his strength and undermined his spirit. He became subject to heart attacks and sensitive to slurs cast on his honor by opportunistic litigants. In 1890 his main patent claims finally suffered "collapse."

"We could no longer deny [our delay in securing a patent]," the inventor wrote from Giessen to Anna, his wife and confidante. "Maybe there was still a possibility of feigning, but the fact is that we did not want to jeopardize our good name. The Supreme Court repeatedly intimated their sympathy to me." He assured his wife that he had "taken the matter most calmly" and sent affectionate salutations to her, their three daughters and son.

During the long court ordeals Otto had fought off personal collapse with frequent rest cures. Now, again near a breakdown, he planned to relax with a visit to Holzhausen on the Heather, his boyhood home.

From the inn Wilhelmina, the inventor's sister, wrote to Anna, "That my brother intends to visit us soon after New Year's is very welcome to us all. . . . In February I will be seventy-seven so August should indeed come . . . otherwise we won't see each other any more."

Her premonition was well founded. During his fifty-eighth year, still planning the visit to his cherished Holzhausen and his adored Wilhelmina, on January 22, 1891, Nikolaus August Otto died peacefully in his sleep at his Cologne home.

Eugen Langen, his partner of twenty-seven years, extolled the "joy of our collaboration." Gottlieb Daimler—

who had left the Deutz firm in 1882 to concentrate on developing a lightweight internal combustion automobile engine—wrote to the widow, "I, too, owe him much. . . . The thoughts he leaves behind remain as a blessing as do also his works."

Otto's work was vastly more important than he could have dreamed. In his letter to Anna, after the "collapse" of his patents, the inventor had stated, "But the fact is that now the dance will start, and all the world will build engines." Exactly that occurred.

Following the Paris Exhibition of 1878 the Otto high-speed "silent" gas engine quickly won recognition as the most efficient stationary engine and was made by many firms. Its inventor lived to obtain only a brief glimpse of the internal combustion engine applied to the motor-car, a great new development facilitated by his four-cycle principle. He saw the first pioneering efforts of Gottlieb Daimler and Carl Benz. But of the engine's use in aircraft Otto had no knowledge.

And only after the inventor's death did the internal combustion engine achieve its greatest victory over steam, when Rudolph Diesel developed the revolutionary engine that bears his name, using the Otto-cycle.

Little known though he is, Nikolaus August Otto is not forgotten. In 1932, on the centenary of his birth, distinguished engineers from all over the world met at Cologne and laid a wreath on his tomb in the Friedhof Melaten. They hailed his invention of the four-stroke engine as the great connecting link between the earlier engine inventions of Street, Brown, Barnett, Barsanti,

Matteucci and Lenoir—and the later developments credited to Clerk, Robson, Daimler, Benz, Diesel and a host of others who played some part in perfecting the internal combustion engine.

Modest Nikolaus Otto would have been the last to claim the title of father of the internal combustion engine. Yet, on that centennial day, great engineers who thoroughly understood his contribution so named him. Citing the millions of engines in powerhouses, factories, ships, motorcars and airplanes working on the Otto-cycle, they declared Otto's feat to be as fundamentally important in the development of the internal combustion engine as Watt's separate condenser had been in the earlier development of the steam engine.

With his separate condenser James Watt removed the bar to a successful steam engine. With his four-stroke or Otto-cycle principle, Nikolaus August Otto forced the internal combustion engine to do man's bidding in the service of men.

Not only did the internal combustion engine fulfill Otto's dream of industrial, agricultural and domestic uses, but it completely revolutionized transportation by land, sea and air. All over the world it created new industries and services pertaining to each method of travel. Few inventions brought such profound changes so quickly after their fruition as did Nikolaus August Otto's internal combustion engine.

- 18 -

CARL BENZ

1844 - 1929

FATHER OF THE AUTOMOBILE INDUSTRY

CARL BENZ was the grandson of a blacksmith and son of a locomotive engineer. That he should bear the title of father of the automobile industry is fitting, for the occupation of the three generations neatly summarizes the nineteenth century's startling advances in mechanics and transportation.

Carl was born November 25, 1844, at Muehldorf near Karlsruhe, Baden, Germany. Just twenty-one years earlier his father, Hans Georg Benz, had been among the many stirred to adventure when George Stephenson's locomotive enabled the Stockton & Darlington Railway to introduce the steam railroad in England. The event marked man's first attainment of mechanical land transportation.

Leaving the Black Forest village of Pfaffenrot, where

his father and grandfather had served as blacksmith and burgomaster, Hans moved to Karlsruhe. He found employment as a locomotive driver on an early German railroad, but an accident cut short his life. His widow and two-year-old Carl survived.

The boy showed early mechanical ability and was graduated in engineering from the Polytechnic Institute. For several subsequent years he worked at the bench in machine shops and factories in Karlsruhe and Stuttgart. Life seemed uneventful.

Then, at twenty-eight, while working as a carriage designer in Stuttgart, Carl married Fräulein Berta Ringer, destined to become the world's first woman motorcar enthusiast. She urged her husband to invest his savings in a Mannheim stationary "gas" engine shop. At night, however, he experimented at converting his regular product to an engine that would power the wheels of a carriage. Secretly he had worked on the idea for five years—since a friend in Stuttgart had taught him to ride a novel contraption called a velocipede. At every step Frau Benz cheered him on.

Faced with dwindling funds, Carl twice took in partners, who exerted constant pressure on him to abandon his foolish dream of an auto-propelled vehicle.

One can understand the doubts that disturbed these sound, "right-thinking" men. The two-stroke "gas" engine of the day had a huge flywheel, burned illuminating gas produced from coal and was used largely for pumping. Easy enough to set one on a vehicle, but then what?

How could power be carried to the wheels? To which

wheels, all or one, front or back? What type of transmission could vary the gear ratio between a slow-running, extremely low-powered engine and the wheels? Direct connecting rods would be scientifically impossible. And even if the wheels could be connected to the power plant, how could the engine be kept running when the vehicle stopped? How could a driver control the r.p.m. of the engine, the speed of the vehicle? How could a railless vehicle be steered? How? How?

"Right-thinking" men asked a hundred such questions and reached the same conclusions. Too bad the Benzes —such a nice couple, and he such a brilliant mechanic— had such crazy ideas!

In 1883 Carl was able to organize Benz & Cie. Rheinische Gasmotorenfabrik—and devote more time to his experiments. Two years later he was ready for a secret trial. He hovered watchfully as workmen pushed from his shop an odd-looking wheeled contraption mounting an engine. He was no longer young. Gray glinted in his blond hair and flowing mustache. Twelve years had passed since he began experimenting in his Mannheim shop; eighteen since he had ridden his friend's velocipede in Stuttgart. And now . . .

Seating himself, he started the engine. Clattering explosions followed, the wheels turned and Frau Benz ran alongside, clapping her hands in wild enthusiasm. Then came erratic sputterings and a sudden stop. The trial was over. However briefly, an internal combustion engine had driven a vehicle.

Benz ordered a carriage, worked intensively for several months and then was confident. No need for secrecy now. Before assembled friends and relatives—including sons Eugen, twelve, and Richard, ten—Frau Benz took a place beside the driver's seat. The flywheel was swung. Not a sound. Tensely the driver instructed his assistants. Then with rapid, echoing explosions the carriage leapt forward, completely out of control. After throwing Herr and Frau Benz clear, the vehicle wrecked itself against a wall.

No ceremony marked the next trial, but again the dauntless Frau sat primly beside her husband while the carriage jerkily moved about one hundred yards before sputtering to a halt. Then came a non-stop spin for a full kilometer, six tenths of a mile, at a speed of twelve kilometers, or seven and two tenths miles per hour!

Benz patented his car January 29, 1886. The papers reveal that it employed a horizontal flywheel belt transmission through a differential with two chains to the wheels. Also, it utilized the four-stroke cycle, only nine years after Nikolaus August Otto had first built it into an engine. Benzine powered a water-jacketed, three-quarter-horsepower engine. Crude as it was, the vehicle embodied many features of today's motorcar that establish it as the granddaddy of them all.

All Mannheim was drawn to the Benz car. Fascination overcame fear of the noisy machine. Crowds watched Benz and his Frau take daily runs in the neighborhood. Throughout Germany headlines followed every appearance.

Inevitably police action came. In Baden Province speeds exceeding six kilometers an hour within a city, or twelve kilometers outside a city, were declared unlawful. The limits equaled walking and slow trotting paces, respectively.

Absurd! Benz persuaded the provincial minister to come to Mannheim. As Benz drove him in his car from the railroad station a horse-drawn milk wagon slowed their pace. Strenuously but vainly Benz tried to pass. The minister became annoyed. Then the inventor remarked that the horseless carriage was a new form of transportation. "It can mean much to everybody if it isn't hobbled to a horse's pace." The official got the point, and the speed limits were revoked. If he suspected that the incident had been arranged between Benz and the milk wagon driver, he was right!

Benz built the first gasoline-powered vehicle, but he did not invent the automobile. It is practically impossible to say who did. Ever since Watt had solved the key problem of the steam engine, many men had tried to make auto, or self-propelled, vehicles by hitching steam power to the wheels of vehicles. Frenchman Nicolas Cugnot in 1769 and Englishman Richard Trevithick in 1802 both had publicly demonstrated their monstrous steam carriages.

For frightening people and animals Cugnot had been jailed. Following Trevithick's "escapade," England had passed the "Red Flag" law. It required that a man carrying a red flag walk in front of any mechanical vehicle operated on a road. In other words, it hobbled engines to a man's slow walking pace. Engines on rails were terrifying enough!

Nevertheless, despite antagonism and restrictions,

men continued to invent crude steam automachines. In fact, by the time Benz and others were working on their gas vehicles, so much progress had been made that trim, French-produced, little steam cars were becoming popular on the roads.

In 1888 Panhard and Levassor, the firm which handled Benz's stationary engines in France, was already producing steam automobiles. But the success of the Benz automobile—the only gasoline motorcar to show at the Paris Exhibition of 1889—induced the firm to undertake its manufacture and improvement. It acted similarly for Gottlieb Daimler, another German, who, independently of Benz, had made and driven a motorcar in the same year as his compatriot.

Some believe Daimler's gas auto invention came first. Others point to the gas motorcar invented as early as 1873 by the Austrian, Siegfried Marcus, and still in possession of the Austrian Automobile Club. But Marcus' experiments were unsuccessful and he abandoned his task after building two vehicles. He left the agelong problem still unsolved.

The Daimler car, which like Benz's vehicle also had many features of the modern automobile, was to far outstrip the latter in the early days because of Daimler's aggressiveness and Benz's conservativeness. Benz never took the wheel at early motorcar races, as other inventors often did to show the merits of their vehicles.

Instead Benz took his Frau and family for rides. The joy they experienced in touring was prophetic of things to come, the essence of the budding popularity of the motorcar. In a way Benz became the symbol of the cap-goggles-and-duster day of the automobile. Others sought speed and power. He was content with pleasure and utility. Thus did Benz introduce the Automobile Age.

Receiving many honors for his engineering achievements, he soon became Dr. Benz.

In the United States the "steamer" also got the jump on the gasoline car even though the Duryea brothers built their "buggyault," probably the first American-built gasoline car, as early as 1892. Haynes and Ford startled Kokomo and Detroit, respectively, with first showings of their gasoline cars in the same year and in the one following.

Moreover, the "electric" car was also in the picture, and many people thought that it would best the steamer and gas car.

It will be seen, then, that at the turn of the century automotive engineers had spawned newborn triplets—steamer, gasoline buggy and electric car. Within fifteen years the steamer and the electric were puny, failing children. But because of its relatively simple mechanism, the availability of its fuel and the manufacturing methods applied to it, the gasoline buggy thrived lustily.

Benz lived to see the automobile "mean much to everybody" as he had predicted to the minister of Baden. However, not in Germany which had sired the motorcar, nor in France which had reared it, did his visionary revolution in transportation materialize. Rather, American industrial genius applied mass production methods to the motorcar, an accomplishment in itself replete with miracles of mechanical and manufacturing innovations.

And, while European motorcar production and use were making strides, in the United States they soared. Mass production shaped Benz's dream of motorizing the family horse and buggy into a reality of pleasure and utility. American industrial methods put the motorcar within the financial reach of the average family, transformed it from a luxury to the attainable, to a necessity. American know-how spearheaded the revolution in transportation which, in its larger aspects, became a social revolution, and spreads yet today to all nations seeking economic and social advancement.

At Munich, in July 1925, the Allgemeine Schnauferlklub, or General Bone-Shaker Club, comprised of pioneer motor enthusiasts, held a rally on the occasion of its twenty-fifth anniversary. Dr. Benz, though eighty-one, was the guest of honor. Seated in his first car, which the Deutsches Museum had released for the day, he and his faithful Frau headed a procession of ancient horseless vehicles. At the following banquet Benz was called the "George Stephenson of the automobile."

Four years later the automobile industry, learning that Benz was feeble, decided to pay him a special tribute. On April 1, 1929, a surprise procession of several hundred cars of all ages and makes from all parts of Germany paraded to Carl Benz Platz in Ladenburg. Thousands gathered in the square before the Benz house. The Frau, sons Eugen and Richard and their wives and sons, along with other relatives, appeared at the windows. But not the man whom the crowd was honoring.

Three days later the *Koelnische Zeitung* sadly reported, " 'The Father of the Automobile,' Dr. Carl Benz, died this evening at Ladenburg."

On Easter Sunday, 1933, the city of Mannheim unveiled a monument to the man who, always supported by his Frau, sedately introduced the Automobile Age.

- 19 -

RUDOLF DIESEL

1858 - 1913

FATHER OF THE DIESEL INDUSTRY

ELEVEN MONTHS before World War I began in Europe, Rudolf Diesel vanished from the British channel steamer *Dresden,* en route from Antwerp to London. His bed had not been slept in. No crewman or passenger had seen the Paris-born German inventor after nightfall. Bound for conferences with British government officials—presumably relative to the use of Diesel power in submarines—he was known to have been carrying important papers. They were missing. The sensational mystery was never definitely solved.

At the time of Diesel's disappearance the full significance of the invention that had made him both famous and controversial could scarcely be measured. But an English editor and engineer friend wrote, "Wait. Twenty years hence he will stand out as a man whose influence on engineering progress has been greater than that of anyone since Watt." The prophecy bore fruit.

From his early years Diesel seemed marked for greatness—of that his parents and Professor Carl von Linde, his teacher and mentor, were certain. His father, a talented bookbinder of Augsburg, Germany, and his mother, a language tutor from Nuremberg, had met in London and renewed their friendship in Paris, where they married. There Rudolf was born March 18, 1858.

The boy grew up sharing his parents' fluency in English, French and German. He was adept at using tools, and intensely interested in machinery, engineering and physics. Often his doting parents openly praised his cleverness and handsome appearance. Striving harder to justify their praise, Rudolf became self-conscious and somewhat vain.

With the outbreak of the Franco-Prussian War in 1870, all Germans were required to leave Paris, and the Diesels moved to London. Never did the little family regain the even tenor of its former life. In the impressionable mind of the twelve-year-old Rudolf, who had thought of himself only as French, the idea of being an unwanted refugee left a permanent scar.

After brief schooling in London, Rudolf lived for three years with an uncle in Augsburg and was graduated, the youngest of his class, from the Industrie Schule, an engineering school. His outstanding record, which is said never to have been equaled, earned him a scholarship at the Technisch Hochschule, a technical college in Munich.

One day Professor von Linde, head of the college and inventor of refrigeration machines then coming into commercial production, ended a lecture, "And so, gentlemen, we must conclude that, considering the great amount of fuel required, existing prime movers produce relatively small power. Class dismissed." This observation on the shortcomings of the steam and gas engines, extant about 1875, shaped Diesel's life.

Graduating with top honors at twenty-one, Diesel took employment with Von Linde's refrigeration firm and built a plant in Paris, where he remained for ten strenuous years. Working long hours, he acquired a knowledge of compressors and problems of compression that was probably unexcelled. But the engineer's letters of that period—quoted in *Diesel, Der Mensch, Das Werk, Das Schicksal,* a notable biography by his son Eugen—speak of his suffering from intense headaches. Constant strain and overwork increased the affliction for the rest of his life.

Diesel remembered Von Linde's remark about existing engines and along with his work strove to produce a new prime mover. His first efforts centered around an ammonia vapor motor, and before the 1889 International Congress of Applied Mechanics, in Paris, he read, in perfect French, a paper on the subject. Soon, however, he turned to the internal combustion engine, which Nikolaus August Otto was bringing to the fore in Germany with his development of the four-stroke cycle.

Two years after taking an assignment to handle Von Linde's business in North Germany, Diesel was ready.

On February 28, 1892, the German Patent Office granted him Patent No. 67207 on "Working Processes for Internal Combustion Engines." Though overwhelmed with applications for such patents, the officials stated that Diesel's idea was *new*.

New it was. Various men had carried the internal combustion engine from a gunpowder experiment to a successful electrically sparked gasoline *explosion* engine. Diesel departed sharply from the accepted trend. His planned engine was still of the internal combustion type, since it converted the heat of natural fuel into work within the cylinder. But it dispensed with the explosive fuel and the carburetor. Instead, the compression of injected air would raise its temperature to a point at which the fuel would ignite as soon as it entered the cylinder, much on the order of grease flashing in a frying pan. With heat ignition a heavy oil, cheaper than gasoline, could be used for fuel.

Diesel considered his invention to be the nearest approach to an ideal heat engine. The great Augsburg Machine Works, to which he first proposed development of the engine, listened, but hesitated. In 1893 Diesel published his arguments in a historic book, *Theory and Construction of a Rational Heat Engine to Replace Steam and the Existing Internal Combustion Engine.* The volume convinced the Augsburg manufactory. With the great Krupp firm sharing the risk, it agreed to pay Diesel 30,000 marks annually to construct his engine.

August 10, 1893, the inventor threw a lever to start his first engine. It exploded violently and almost killed him.

But Diesel had proved his point. Heat resulting from compression would ignite the fuel. He was happy!

While recovering from his injuries the inventor toiled at designing and building a new engine. Two years later, June 1895—after many alternate periods of depression and exhilaration—he confidently faced brake trials. What should he call his new engine—Beta, Delta, Excelsior? He consulted his wife, Martha.

In Paris, like his father before him, Rudolf had met and married—on November 15, 1883—a young Fräulein. Martha Frasche was a tutor in the family of a merchant and fluent in German, French and English. Their three children had been born in France, and Martha became a particularly close associate who accompanied him on many of his later travels. She did not hesitate. "Call it Diesel," she said.

The tests were made and the engine performed satisfactorily. Diesel's fame spread rapidly through the engineering world. Eager to see and learn, representatives from leading firms the world over thronged to Augsburg. Prosperity supplemented fame.

Far from being relieved of strain, however, the inventor was engulfed with troubles. Krupp and other firms had begun production of the engine, but anti-Diesel factions blossomed in various factories. Much of the industry and many of the workers favored steam power and feared the interloper. Complaints about the operation of his engine poured down upon him. Accusations that he had sold his patent rights before perfecting his engine were widespread.

To unsnarl problems relative to his licenses Diesel traveled to all parts of the world. He propounded his discovery to learned societies. He fought numerous suits as to the originality of his patents. Almost constantly he faced virulent criticism and threats of litigation. The charges heaped upon his sensitive nature took a severe toll, and in 1898 he suffered a breakdown.

Thereafter his painful headaches increased in frequency and in violence. Yet, his son writes, never did the inventor betray his feelings. Nothing disturbed his delicate, classic features set off by an inevitable *pince-nez*. Always his scholarly and patrician bearing, his straightforward statements, discomfited his enemies. Diesel became, in fact, the exemplar of his own words: "The inventor must be an optimist, since the full driving power of an idea is to be found only in the mind of the originator. He alone has the sacred fire to push it through."

From a man of Diesel's brilliance only further accomplishment could be anticipated.

He was merely fifty-five when he boarded the *Dresden* at Antwerp on the night of September 26, 1913. Two friends were accompanying him on his mission to England. Cheerfully he bade them good evening and retired to his cabin. He was never seen again.

What happened is conjecture, for he left no notes. The highly important papers may have been upon his person when, in the iron grasp of one of his attacks, excruciating agony momentarily smothered his "sacred fire" and drove him to the vessel's rail.

A famous scientist, widely acquainted and traveled, Diesel had been essentially a family man. He had withheld from his wife and children his fear of financial ruin. Not until after his death did they learn that he had lost a million marks in land deals and another fortune in oil stocks. Little remained.

The legacy of boundless power, which Diesel left to our industrial age, all but obliterates his tragic end. A year before his disappearance the inventor, in his faultless English, had told an audience of American engineers, "Nowhere in the world are the possibilities for this prime mover as great as in this country." His prophecy came true. For largely in America the modern two-cycle engine, which has tremendously increased the reliability and flexibility of the Diesel, was developed.

Could the inventor return to the United States today he would find "Diesel" and "Dieselization" incorporated into our language, and that American engineers and manufacturers have ranged beyond the frontiers of his vision, outstripping the world.

Employed today in ships, trucks, buses and road-building equipment, the Diesel engine has revolutionized marine and highway transportation. Streamlined Diesel-electric locomotives have brought renewed prosperity to railroads. Diesel tractors have blazed a trail to the mechanized farm, an agricultural revolution. In manufacturing and construction, indeed in almost every industry—the ever present Diesel hums "power."

Thus, during his pain-ravaged life, Rudolf Diesel fulfilled the dream of his parents and of Professor von

Linde. Destined for greatness, the boy went far. And thus, after his tragic death, he bore out the prophecy of his British engineer-editor friend that he would "stand out as a man whose influence in engineering progress has been greater than that of anyone since Watt."

WILBUR WRIGHT

1867 - 1912

ORVILLE WRIGHT

1871 - 1948

FATHERS OF THE AIRPLANE INDUSTRY

WILBUR, third son of Milton and Susan Wright, was born April 16, 1867, at Millville, Indiana. Two years later the family moved to Dayton, Ohio, taking a small dwelling on Hawthorne Street which was to be its home for more than four decades. In that house Orville came into the world August 19, 1871, and on his third birthday Katharine was born. In the same home Susan, the mother, died when Wilbur was twenty-two and Orville eighteen.

By that time Milton, a former circuit-riding preacher, had become a bishop of the United Brethren Church. Already the first and second boys had married and left the fold, but Katharine remained at home. An Oberlin graduate, unmarried and a high school teacher, she was assisted in keeping house for her widowed father and two bachelor brothers by a maid, "faithful Carrie."

Only a few blocks away was the Wright Cycle Company shop which Wilbur and Orville had chosen to set up rather than finish high school. In a second shop behind their first the brother mechanics quietly spent much time and labor in building kites for their own amusement—or so it seemed.

Milton Wright's teachings and his parson's pay had inculcated habits of devotion and thrift in his sons. As boys they preferred reading for recreation. With their occasional play, they often mixed business—seldom, for instance, did their neighborhood circuses fail to make a profit. They liked games that stimulated their thinking, and they inherited their father's considerable mechanical bent. To encourage that trait Bishop Milton gave the boys, way back in the 1870s, a toy Pénaud heliocopter. The French inventor's little models, powered with twisted rubber bands, had become popular the world over. The father's choice was providential. Soon his sons were deeply studying the little-known science of aerodynamics.

Wilbur and Orville read all they could find about the glider men: Mouillard, the Frenchman, who, in recording his thirty years of bird study, had traced outlines of many birds' wings on paper and expounded theories as to how birds fly; and Lilienthal, the German birdman, who donned wings, raced down sand hills and coasted into the air until 1896, when he fatally crashed.

That same year the brothers avidly pored over accounts of the wonderful gliding tests made on the shores of Lake Michigan by the Americans Octave Chanute and A. M. Herring.

For, oddly enough, the two bicycle mechanics—circumspect models of industriousness and caution that they were—themselves wanted to be glider men, to build their own machines, to fly.

Lilienthal's death only strengthened their determination. The German had balanced his machine merely by shifting his body. But, as Orville wrote later, believing this method "incapable of expansion to meet the requirements of flight," the brothers set about developing "a more effective system."

Dedicated and absorbed in studies and experiments, they had little time for many normal youthful interests. When attractive Oberlin classmates visited Katharine,

she berated her brothers for neglecting her guests. Wedded to their work, naturally retiring, even shy, the two men remained lifelong bachelors.

During 1900, quietly—but not secretly—Wilbur and Orville began glider experiments on the lonely, windswept sands of Kitty Hawk, North Carolina. Across the sound stood deserted Roanoke Island, site of Sir Walter Raleigh's "Lost Colony."

Intensively Wilbur and Orville searched for the secret of equilibrium—a better method of balancing, a way of making air lift the falling wing of a machine whenever it tilted to one side. Finally they devised a method of warping the wings at the trailing edge. Then, when a wing dropped below horizontal, the pilot moved a control, causing the trailing edge to bend a bit downward, thus offering increased lift to that side. Simultaneously, the wing on the rising side was warped upward to reduce the lift, thus causing the rising side to drop. The combined forces tended to balance the plane. In a word, the Wrights gave their machine a third axis of control which prevented side-to-side seesawing.

Now the brothers, expert with their gliders, were ready to install an engine—to take the all-important step that would advance them from glider men to birdmen.

Reduce the ratio of weight to horsepower—that was their problem. They had calculated the necessary specifications—an eight-horsepower gasoline engine weighing no more than two hundred pounds. Finding the manufacturers unable or unwilling to produce one, the brothers built their own four-cylinder engine which, under test, developed sixteen horsepower for a few seconds before falling off to twelve.

⸙ Early on the morning of December 17, 1903, with the wind blowing at twenty-seven miles per hour, the wheelless gasoline-powered plane was launched from a separate wheeled crossbeam. Orville, lying flat, was at the controls, and, before reaching the end of the rail, he tilted the horizontal rudder. The plane rose in full flight, under its own power with no reduction in speed at seven miles per hour. Wilbur moved along behind, as the machine spanned about 120 feet in twelve seconds. Its landing point was as high as its take-off.

Wilbur made the next flight of 13 seconds, and Orville the third of a quarter minute. Then, at noon, Wilbur took off again. Airborne for fifty-nine seconds, he had traveled 852 feet. After Wilbur alighted, a gust of wind tumbled the plane over several times, permanently damaging it.

Not a single reporter was present to see and record, to get the big scoop—FIRST SUCCESSFUL AIRPLANE FLIGHT BY MAN IN HISTORY.

Yet, up on the Potomac River only nine days earlier, December 8, 1903, newspapermen had crowded around a houseboat from which Dr. Samuel Pierpont Langley had launched his much-heralded plane. In 1896, at sixty-two, Dr. Langley, secretary of the Smithsonian Institution in Washington, had built a wonderful steam-driven model of a flying machine, somewhat larger than an eagle. It flew 3000 feet, winning its designer a $50,000 congressional appropriation to build a man-carrying plane. This machine was the result—a second test, for the machine's first attempt had failed. And the reporters saw and recorded another failure. Without flying, the machine plunged into the water and the wreck made a sensational story. Three years later Langley was to die of a broken heart, and aviation was to struggle long under a cloud of doubt. If a gifted scientist could not succeed, what could be expected of a couple of untrained bicycle mechanics?

The Wrights made the flying machine practical by providing the link needed to establish equilibrium—the missing link which had cost Lilienthal his life. They developed a system of balance in which the center of gravity remained constant. This system, generally known as lateral control, they patented.

Furthermore, in their Dayton workshop the brothers set up a small wind tunnel. Working far into the nights, they measured the lift and drag of a great number of different-shaped airfoils at angles from zero to forty-five degrees. In short, in their experiments and calculations, the two mechanical geniuses, neither of whom had completed high school, found that almost all of the existing "scientific" data in the field of aerodynamics were untrustworthy! Not only did the Wrights make it possible for man to fulfill his long-felt wish to become airborne, and not only were they the first to fly a motor-driven plane—their primary contribution to aviation was to give the fundamentals of safety to the vehicle of the air.

Perhaps it was no accident that the inventors of the airplane were cautious, observant and, above all, exact men.

No daredevil flyers—the Wrights. Yet, once they believed their machine developed to the stage of usefulness, they spent several years "barnstorming," or, as
Orville called it, "finding a market." In 1908 Wilbur's
flights at Le Mans and Pau, France, and, later, at Rome,
left the world gasping and agape. Along with the multitudes, they attracted the kings of England, Spain and
Italy.

England, France, Germany and Italy were first to recognize the Wrights' achievement. And today to learn that
doubt ever existed that the Wright brothers fathered
flight takes us by surprise. The sensitive, unworldly
brothers were deeply offended by the lack of interest of
U.S. government officials in their invention. Successful
in contracting for planes with foreign governments,
nevertheless, the brothers held open the door for the
United States. Finally, and somewhat belatedly, their
patriotism was rewarded. A Wright plane was the first
adopted by the United States Army, and the brothers
were the first instructors of our Army fliers.

Always, beneath their mild, shy exteriors, the Wrights
were men of strong convictions with courage to fight for
their beliefs. They prospered beyond their rosiest
dreams. Yet they disliked business. Once the Wright
Company was well established they planned to resign
and resume their beloved research. Meanwhile, in Oak-
wood, a Dayton suburb, they started a mansion they
called Hawthorn Hill. Wilbur never saw it finished, for
he died May 30, 1912, of typhoid fever complicated by
patent suit worries.

In April 1914 the subdued family left its old home for

Hawthorn Hill. Orville had succeeded Wilbur as president of the company, but not until 1915 did he feel that he could resign. On April 3, 1917, Bishop Wright died at the age of eighty-nine. (At eighty-two he had made his first flight, with Orville piloting.)

Now, of the original household, only Orville, Katharine and "faithful Carrie" remained. In 1926 Katharine married and left her brother in the good hands of Carrie. Lonely, retiring and immersed in research as he was, Orville was no recluse. He became the elder statesman of aviation, gladly responding to numerous inquiries. Several devoted and admiring nephews and nieces—children of the older brothers who had married—brightened his loneliness.

Mellowing with the years, Orville shyly opened his arms to his friends. His dry humor took on a puckish flavor. "I wonder if this whole thing isn't a mistake," he said to a congressman at the cornerstone laying of the Wright Memorial Shaft at Kitty Hawk.

So life went on with Orville the recipient of honors to the Wright brothers, showered by his own and many other nations. And before Orville died, January 30, 1948, he had seen the "miracle at Kitty Hawk" expand to an established form of transportation. Airmail routes had come and grown into passenger and freight lines running on schedule. Great airports dotted the landscape, and automatic beacons marked the way for night flying. Floodlighting made night traffic possible, the radio compass and other instruments were aiding aerial navigation and blind flying. Today the Wrights are honored everywhere as the fathers of the airplane industry.

Aviation's many advances from the status of a risky stunt to an accepted mode of everyday transportation all reflect the exactness that was the most conspicuous quality of the fathers of the airplane industry. Continuous research has produced safety in tested planes as well as in scientific flying and landing devices. The sensational—like Langley's wreck—still catches the headlines, but the great triumph of the Wrights and of succeeding researchers is evidenced on every hand, in every sky.

Were they here today, the Wrights' greatest satisfaction would be in knowing that the millions of passengers carried on airlines throughout the world can truthfully be told that they are indulging in the safest form of travel.

The Wrights did more than conquer the air with their first flight at Kitty Hawk. They altered the course of history. Since the day when Sir Walter Raleigh had landed his colonists on bleak Roanoke Island, the world had undergone startling changes. But it was still an earthbound world. The Wrights ushered in the twentieth century, and with it came many of the technical, political and social changes that promise to make it the most revolutionary epoch in the annals of man.

In all of industrial history, few heritages to mankind have ever had greater significance than the airplane, left to the world by two modest, hard-working, painstaking bicycle mechanics.

- 21 -

ALEXANDER GRAHAM BELL

1847 - 1922

FATHER OF THE TELEPHONE

IN THE EARLY 1870s a young man named Alexander Graham Bell taught at Sarah Fuller's Boston School for the Deaf. He was Scottish, born in Edinburgh, March 3, 1847, but had come to Boston by way of London and Canada. Disaster had struck the Bell family in England, where Graham's older and younger brothers had died of tuberculosis. The doctor's verdict that Graham would be the next victim of this disease called for an immediate decision. Graham's father, Alexander Melville Bell, unhesitatingly sacrificed his business and moved his family to the healthy climate of Brantford, Ontario, in Canada.

This was the only period of leisure Graham was to know. "I dreamed away the afternoons on my sofa seat in a cozy woodland nook in luxurious idleness," he later recalled. His father had taken a job as a teacher of elocution at Queen's College in Kingston, and young Graham was also fascinated with new methods of teaching speech. When the elder Bell received an offer from Sarah Fuller's school, Graham, who had recovered his health, was sent in his father's place. He filled the bill so well that he was soon teaching as many as four hundred English syllables in a few weeks to deaf-mute children who had failed to learn anything in two or three years by other methods of teaching.

Years later one of his fellow teachers remembered him with the nine-year-old deaf, dumb and blind Helen Keller on his lap. He would converse with her by tapping out Morse telegraph code messages on the back of her hand. Helen would smile in obvious delight as she understood what he was saying to her. It may be suspected that he was saying something funny. For this man had a streak of whimsy in him, humor of a sort that even enjoys a joke on oneself.

If Helen Keller had had sight and had been born only deaf and dumb, he might have used another method with her, called "visible speech," invented by his father and adopted by schools throughout the United Kingdom. It was an oral method as opposed to sign language. To give or to save the power of speech, to challenge the idea that the deaf have no place in normal society, was, for this man, a lifelong crusade. Intense personal reasons as well as conviction based on study and skill moved him.

He and his father had watched his mother gradually

lose her hearing. A friend, writing of a later period when she was entirely deaf, tells of Graham—himself an accomplished musician (he could never remember when he could not play the piano)—playing for her while she sat with her ear pressed against the wood of the sounding board. Also he was engaged to Mabel Hubbard, daughter of Gardiner Hubbard, a Boston attorney. She had been stricken with deafness when a child of four, from scarlet fever. Her parents had sent the child to Germany where oral treatment had saved her power of speech. Gardiner Hubbard had succeeded in getting the Massachusetts legislature to pass a bill establishing an oral school for the deaf, against the violent opposition of sign-language educators and those who believed that any attempt to teach deaf mutes to speak flouted the laws of Providence. The leader in the battle had found a staunch and ardent lieutenant in young Bell.

Mabel was only sixteen. Graham was twenty-six. He would wait a couple of years. Besides, he had no money. He got a better-paying job as professor of vocal physiology in Boston University's School of Oratory. He tutored on the side. That was how he met Thomas Sanders, a civic-minded Boston businessman—by tutoring little Georgie Sanders, born a deaf mute. One would think that Alexander Graham Bell had found his niche in teaching, but at nights and between classes and tutoring he worked on his "talking machine."

He had progressed far from the experiments he had done with the help of his brothers in Scotland in his early youth—from their "talking head," for instance. It

was shaped like a human skull, and when brother Melville moved its jaws and blew through the tin "windpipe," it said "Mama." The youngster had also done experiments with his trained Skye terrier. When he pressed the dog's mouth and vocal cords to shape the "words," it growled: "Ow ah oo, Ga-ma-ma," meaning "How are you, Grandmother?"

Graham Bell's mind was instinctively inventive. From an idea he had for a machine to help teach speech had grown the thought of developing one that would send more than one telegraph message and more than one tone over one wire at the same time; that is, a "harmonic telegraph." The idea of a telephone was not new. It had even been named by another inventor. Inventors by the score in many countries had been working on talking telegraphs ever since Morse's invention of the telegraph a quarter of a century before. Now Bell's great fear was that somebody would beat him to the finish line. From Mabel Hubbard's father and Georgie Sander's father he found such ready backing (Sanders to the extent of running $100,000 in debt and risking bankruptcy) that he took a leave of absence from teaching to devote full time to developing his invention.

How Graham Bell with his assistant, a mechanic and electrician named Thomas A. Watson, working first in the electrical shop of Charles Williams, Jr., in Court Street and then in their boardinghouse on Essex Street, made their first telephone call is an oft-told tale. Their experimental instrument worked by means of sound vibrations conducted electrically over wire, using for transmitter a single "diaphragm" and for receiver a reproduction of the human ear. The words uttered early in the evening of March 3, 1876, by Bell from his bedroom to his cellar "laboratory" in Essex Place: "Mr. Watson, come here. I want you," and the scene of the excited young assistant rushing in and saying: "It was clear! I have never heard it so clear before," have become part of our American folklore.

The first of the four famous patents of Alexander Graham Bell was granted March 7, 1876, with Watson participating. Hubbard, Sanders and Bell agreed to share equally if anything came of the invention. Bell's demonstration tours, financed by Hubbard and Sanders; the fortunate accident that Emperor Dom Pedro of Brazil had seen a demonstration and insisted on a belated showing of Bell's telephone to a committee of the world's leading scientists at the Philadelphia Centennial Exposition in 1876; the wave of favorable publicity; the eager demand for the telephone through which Bell and Watson were now saluting each other with the words, "Ahoy, are you there?" using both ends of the wire; the sale of the patents to the New England Telephone Company and the Bell Telephone Company in 1878; the organization of the national Bell Telephone System the following year—all were succeeding fast-moving events.

Through his novel experiments, plus his knowledge of music and human speech and hearing, Bell found the way to the telephone. His feat has been called a masterpiece of inventive reasoning. But that a teacher of the deaf should have done this is not as fantastic as it would seem when one realizes that the telephone is a mechanical ear. As if predestined, Bell gave the American telephone system his name. A bell became its symbol. The telephone began to ring in offices and homes throughout the land. After a while the answering voice dropped Bell's jolly "Ahoy" for a prosaic "Hello."

Oddly however, unlike the story of most fathers of industry, Bell did not figure in the perfecting of the device that had so much enthralled him. He did not stick through the "pioneering years" as did his father-in-law and Sanders and his aid, Watson, who became general manager of the early Bell system. His contribution was the four basic patents and time given cheerfully and ungrudgingly during the following years on the witness stand in defense of those patents. (Altogether more than six hundred suits were filed to protect his patents; several reached the Supreme Court, and Bell's rights were upheld in every one of them.) The man who had scored the break-through then blithely turned to other things. He had no business connection with the rapidly expanding Bell system after 1880.

As a wedding present he gave to Mabel Hubbard, whom he married July 11, 1877, his one-third share in the telephone, which was to make her rich and give her a chance to humor her husband's fancy in invention. Their home in Washington and beautiful summer estate at Beinn Bhreagh, Cape Breton, Nova Scotia, became a gathering place for scientists. Bell gave his name to what gradually developed into one of the world's finest research organizations, Bell Laboratories, which one might think would have drawn him into the orbit of its fascinating and varied projects. Not a bit of it. He established his own laboratories, if you please!

One was the Volta Laboratory at Washington, started with the 50,000 francs he received from the French government in 1880 as winner of the Volta prize for his invention of the telephone. Volta researchers took out basic patents for phonograph recording on wax cylinders and discs, selling them to an operating company which launched the recording industry as it is known today in the United States. With his share of the profits, Bell established the Volta Bureau for the study of deafness, which still carries on in Washington, D.C.

Bell's other laboratory was more informal. To Beinn Bhreagh he attracted a group of young men interested in aviation, one of whom was Glenn Curtiss. Bell himself found the greatest outlet for his ardent inventive zeal in the field of aviation. While on his honeymoon in London he had made notes and drawings on the flight of hooded crows. Lord Kelvin, famous British physicist, tried to dissuade him from giving his valuable time and resources to such a hopeless idea as a flying machine. Nevertheless, he contributed $5000 for Professor Langley's experiments, backing—as a racing man would say— the wrong horse.

Langley's attempted flight ended in disaster, but not long afterward the Wright brothers were successful at Kitty Hawk. Glenn Curtiss then became a leading competitor of the Wrights through the Aerial Experiment Association. This association was financed by Mabel

Bell; and her husband was an enthusiastic member of the group. It backed the famous flights of Curtiss, "Casey" Baldwin and other pioneers at Hammondsport, New York, and at Beinn Bhreagh. However, perhaps the outstanding achievement of the Bells' Aerial Experiment Association was in research—the development of the aileron, which is fundamental to all airplane construction today.

Bell's own researches went into any field that caught his fancy. Nothing was too big or too small to attract his interest. A story is told of his dropping a cat from the veranda of his home at Beinn Bhreagh while Professor Langley, then secretary of the Smithsonian Institution, and Simon Newcomb, the astronomer, on all fours below watched carefully to determine why a cat always landed on its feet.

Only once did his later experiments take him close to the telephone. With Sumner Tainter, a maker of optical instruments in Washington, he worked on a method of telephoning over a beam of light. Nothing much came of this "photophone," but it used a method of electromagnetic radiation in a manner to which the "radio" is applied today. He also spent considerable time on what he called a "spectrophone," as he searched for a possible method of identifying invisible emanations of sound.

Bell helped finance and served as president of the National Geographic Society from 1898 to 1903. He was instrumental in building its magazine into a national institution. He was on the board of regents of the Smithsonian Institution. He was a great drawing card as a speaker at dinners and public events.

When he talked through his original telephone box from the offices of the American Telephone & Telegraph Company's building in New York at a ceremony celebrating the first transcontinental telephone connection, in 1912, he repeated one of the shortest and most important speeches of his long life: "Mr. Watson, come here. I want you." This time, however, Watson, his old assistant, was at the other end of the line in San Francisco fifteen hundred miles away!

Often he spoke at schools and colleges. He once said to a group of students: "I don't know whether all fish make sounds or not, but there are some fish that do. . . . Why should they have ears if there is nothing for them to hear? Of this we may be certain . . . that there is a whole world of sound beneath the waves, waiting to be explored, perhaps by some of you." To another group: "Can you tell whether one smell is just twice as strong as another? . . . Until you can measure their likenesses and differences, you can have no science of odor. If you are ambitious to found a new science, measure a smell."

There was no end to his interests or to the originality of his thinking. The Bell Company estimates that during his lifetime Alexander Graham Bell wrote some sixty-five published papers and speeches on subjects relating to the training of the deaf to speak; some twenty on the telephone, the photophone and the spectrophone; four on medical and surgical subjects; four on eugenics and longevity; six on his experiments in sheep raising in Nova Scotia; eight on aerial locomotion; six on miscellaneous inventions; and nine on general subjects.

Late in life he became interested in the heating and ventilating of houses, suggesting several points in construction to aid air conditioning. He advocated action pictures long before the vogue of the comic strip, and even engaged a young artist to carry out the idea.

Alexander Graham Bell had fun. He followed his own advice: "Don't keep forever on the public road, going only where others have gone. . . . Leave the beaten path and dive into the woods."

Many nations honored him with medals and decorations. He received honorary degrees from American, Canadian, English, Scottish and German universities. Of course, the telephone overshadowed all his inventions, yet he told his family he would rather be remembered as a teacher of the deaf than as the telephone's inventor.

During those early years in Boston, Bell applied for United States citizenship. His first papers were dated October 27, 1874. He was admitted to citizenship at Washington, November 10, 1882. In a public address on the occasion of the centennial of President Washington's signing of the U. S. Patent Law, the inventor of the telephone said: "The invention of this country, of a new form of government, and the production of the Constitution of the United States, must stand as one of the most remarkable inventions in the history of man."

When he died, August 2, 1922, at Beinn Bhreagh, telephones throughout the Bell system were silenced for two minutes. The epitaph on his grave at Beinn Bhreagh reads, as he had requested: "Born in Edinburgh : : : :

Died a citizen of the U.S.A.! : : :"

Bell's invention—the telephone—changed the face of the world. Like the airplane, it made the world smaller. And now the telephone aids and is aided by man's venture into outer space. There is a slogan in the Bell Laboratories at Murray Hill, New Jersey, that research in communications of the future is today's business. That business runs the gamut from submarine sonar to radio voices of our satellites flying out in space, in anticipation of calls to future Watsons light-years away.

- 22 -

GUGLIELMO MARCONI

1874 - 1937

FATHER OF WIRELESS TELEGRAPHY

FEW GREAT INVENTORS have been born in palaces. The fact that Guglielmo Marconi, father of wireless telegraphy, first saw the light of day in Palazzo Marescalchi, the family's town house in Bologna, Italy, alone would set him apart from the struggling inventor of familiar pattern. A plaque on the palace gate proudly gives the day—April 25, 1874. But the Villa Griffone, the family's ancestral home in the country at Pontecchio, became far more famous than the palace. There, in a great attic reserved for him at the insistence of his mother, the young Marconi made his great discovery.

The inventor's father, Giuseppe, ran the ancestral estates in a very businesslike way. He had first met the boy's mother when she was a music student at Bologna. Annie Jameson was descended from a Scotch-Irish family which had settled in County Wexford, Ireland, and there were palaces on her side of the family too. She was Giuseppe's second wife, much younger than he. She had taken his son Luigi into the fold, to which she had added two sons: Alfonso and, ten years later, Guglielmo, whom, as he was the youngest, she was apt to spoil.

At least Giuseppe sometimes thought so when he saw the lights burning all night in the locked attic room or tripped over wires that led to aerials in the chestnuts of the beautiful gardens of Villa Griffone. Only the boy had the key to his "laboratory." But often willingly working for him were his half brother and brother—and the gardener and coachman. Giuseppe was willing to humor his wife and youngest son, both adored by him, but within certain limits.

When he was only nineteen years old the boy had developed a notion. With his brothers, he was climbing in the Italian Alps, but his thoughts were far away—on Heinrich Hertz, the German physicist, of whose death he had just read. Suddenly Guglielmo declared that he was sure it was possible for signals—voices, even—to be carried from place to place through the air by Hertzian waves, *without wires*. Perhaps, thought his father, it was time to call a halt to this dreaming. However, every time Giuseppe tried to do so his wife would plead, "Just a little more time, and I'm sure he'll do it."

Now it was 1895, and Guglielmo was twenty-one. His early education had been taken care of by his mother and private tutors. He showed great powers of concen-

tration and had become interested in chemistry and physics. He had pursued these studies at the Institute Cavellero at Florence, then at Leghorn Technical Institute, to such good purpose that Professor Rosa, famous physicist and lecturer at the university, was giving him private lessons.

He was a slender, dark, handsome boy, serious-minded and always more interested in his experiments than in play. He was very methodical, had a good head on his shoulders. All this his father had to admit, despite the "dream." So he consented when his wife pleaded with him to keep Villa Griffone open that winter, so that the boy's experiment in the cold attic would not be interrupted.

Young Marconi had become obsessed with his idea through reading an article about Heinrich Hertz and his discovery, in 1885–89, that electric waves traveled through space at a definite speed. In the field of communication much had happened in the last half century. The electromagnetic recording telegraph, invented by the American, Samuel F. B. Morse, with the Morse code of dots and dashes, was well established in many parts of the world. The telephone of the Canadian Alexander Graham Bell, was being widely installed. But both required an extensive network of wires for transmission.

Hertz's discovery suggested that the air could be used as a conductor of electricity. Yet in all the approximately ten years since, nobody had been able to find out how. The German physicist had used a metal hoop which had a small gap at one side for detecting the waves radiated from his transmitting "oscillator." Minute sparks crossed the gap. This proved, according to the inventor, that electric waves when radiated in space could be detected by means of a metal loop. The theory was the basis of Marconi's experiments in which he used apparatus not unlike that of Hertz.

"It seemed to me at the time," Marconi said years later, "that if this radiation could be increased, developed and controlled, it would most certainly be possible to signal across space for very considerable distances." The wonder to him was that some great inventive brain had not yet discovered so obvious a solution. Early one December morning in 1895 he woke his mother. "Come, Mother, let me show you." He pressed a key that stood on a small table. From the far end of the attic, thirty feet away, an electric bell faintly tinkled.

Before the winter's end Giuseppe participated in a joyful family ceremony. His son's wireless instrument was operating a Morse telegraph key, and crude dots and dashes could be heard over the hill, a mile away! Marconi had succeeded in making improvements on a Hertzian oscillator and on a type of coherer, or receiving device, developed by the Englishman, Professor Branly. By developing a magnetic detector in which an iron wire band was kept rotating through coils, he could receive the signal from an aerial wire. And by magnets which kept the iron tape in proper condition he could induce an increased signal.

Thus Guglielmo Marconi brought the air into the "wireless" domain of communication, eliminating the cost and inflexibility of a permanent network of wires. With almost the speed of electricity itself, he strode with "spark telegraphy," from thirty feet across the attic to a mile across the garden in 1896; to twenty-three miles across the English Channel (from England to France) in 1899; to eighteen hundred miles across the Atlantic (from Poldhu, Ireland, to St. John's, Newfoundland) in 1901; to three thousand miles (from Poldhu to Cape Cod, Massachusetts) in 1905; to six thousand miles (from Punta Arenas, Chile, to Liverpool) in 1910.

The message that crossed the Atlantic in 1901 was the letter S, relayed by Bell's newfangled telephone from remote St. John's to a breathless, waiting world. When, in the following year, the American Institute of Electrical Engineers honored Marconi in New York, Dr. Bell sat at his right. Marconi was only twenty-eight.

Even before his transatlantic achievement he had become world-famous. For "wireless" carried the fascination, mystery, skepticism, even superstitious fears, that nuclear power and missiles and space travel invoke in many today. Many asked then, Was this strange thing, wireless, that gave off sparks causing their aches and pains? Wasn't it "interfering with nature"? To send messages from ship to shore, from ship to ship, with no physical connection, no wires was—well, fantastic, spooky.

Wireless made news. From his first critical test upon the roof of the General Post Office in London to a receiving station he had erected on the Thames Embankment, Marconi and "wireless"—the names became synonymous

—were front-page copy, it seemed, as then the chief use of wireless was on ships or lighthouses to send out the maritime signal of distress, the dreaded "SOS."

From his first test, the governments of one great power after another sought Marconi out for rights to his invention. He patented it in England in 1896 but for patriotic reasons he gave certain rights to his native country without compensation. His mother had high connections in Great Britain, and he had none of the difficulties that usually plague inventors in attracting money needed for improving and developing an original patent. Almost immediately he formed in England what would become the great Marconi Wireless Telegraph Company. It soon attracted men who would become famous in their own right as inventors, researchers and administrators in this new field.

Marconi himself made demonstrations before royalty on their yachts at regattas and races or in connection with maneuvers of war vessels. But more often he was to be found at some spot along a bleak and sea-lashed coast setting up a "pole"—a wireless tower. Or he was at sea on a ship or perhaps visiting the lightships of the famous Trinity House Brethren, Britain's aid-to-navigation service, testing their wireless installations.

"If destiny hadn't made me an inventor," he often said, "surely I would have been a sailor." His love of the sea could now be gratified, and after the First World War he had his own 220-foot yacht, *Rovenska*—later famous as the *Elettra*, his "floating laboratory." It might be seen poking its nose into any harbor where there were Marconi wireless masts—a world-wide range.

The First World War had expanded the use and range of wireless greatly, not only on ships but on land. The Marconi Company trained thousands of wireless operators in a school it established in London which is now Chesholm College. "Marconi operators" were on ships on every one of the seven seas. One outcome of the *Titanic* disaster in 1912, when, though there was great loss of life, seven hundred persons were saved owing to wireless, was the compulsory extension of wireless telegraphy to all merchant vessels.

Moreover, by the end of the war Marconi's dream of "voices through the air" had come true. Conversations by Marconi wireless across the Atlantic began in 1920. No longer was wireless confined to distress signals, weather reports and gale warnings. Like passengers on the ocean liners, the busy inventor on the *Rovenska* relaxed to concerts at sea, broadcast from land stations.

Though keenly interested in the offshoot of wireless which became known as "radio" and which eventually absorbed the name of its parent, Marconi stuck single-mindedly to technical problems of wireless. During the war he had served in the Italian army and navy and as a consultant for the Allies on wireless matters. In his early researches he had demonstrated that short waves could be directed in a beam. He went thoroughly into his old "beam" theory as offering the best means of world-wide wireless transmission.

He secured the British government's backing for the Marconi Company in the project. In 1924 the government could make a sensational announcement. It was ready to establish communication to all parts of the empire by short waves under the beam system. This method brought about almost as great a revolution in the world of wireless as Marconi's first signal across the Atlantic a quarter of a century before.

The inventor then concentrated on increasing the efficiency of wireless telephone. He had stirred the world by his successful wireless telephone test between England and Australia, a distance of twelve thousand miles, in 1924. He finally gave primary study to the possibilities of microwaves, which are unaffected by fog and offer a high degree of secrecy.

Marconi lived until 1937. Meticulous in dress, rather formal, retiring, even shy, some people called him cold, aloof. Yet he made fast friends among his associates and had their loyalty. He held important business posts, read papers before many scientific societies, served as president of not a few such societies, and had a wide acquaintance in many countries. He spoke fluently not only Italian and English but also French.

He was practical, painstaking, punctual, regular in his habits. Though he dealt in magic itself, yet he neither wanted nor expected "rabbits out of a hat." He never faltered when he found that much intensive research would be required to make his dream come true. His confidence never wavered.

Like every successful inventor, he was plagued with lawsuits and had to spend much time in courtrooms and before commissions. He was sensitive to criticism. Sometimes he lost his calm, but seldom a lawsuit, and never an important one. And he won the admiration of the peoples of many nations.

Giuseppe Marconi, his father, lived not only to see his son's transatlantic wireless achievement but to find him heading the largest wireless company in the world—and running it efficiently. For Guglielmo was the rare inventor who also possessed a good business head. Before her death in 1920 his mother saw him awarded many honors by societies, universities and nations, including the Nobel prize for physics. (In 1929 the king of Italy created him a hereditary marquis.)

Indeed, Marconi is the inventor "set apart." Thomas A. Edison, a long-time American friend whom Marconi often visited at his home and famous laboratory at Orange, New Jersey, unpunctual, untidy in his "Mother Hubbard" and with mussed hair, the man with over a thousand patents in any number of fields, was much more typical. Marconi's patents, although they numbered more than one hundred, were practically all in one field. Did the mastery of world-wide wireless communication call for just his combination of adventurous spirit and strict dedication to one ideal?

In 1927 the fifty-three-year-old inventor married Countess Maria Cristina Bezzi Scali, twenty-three-year-old daughter of Count Francesco Bessi Scali of Rome, and they lived mostly on his yacht. Their daughter, born in 1930, they named *Elettra*. They rechristened the yacht with the same name and provided a child's cabin amidships.

The family did not live entirely at sea, but Marconi always had to be near, if not on, the sea. The Villa Griffone at Pontecchio remained the family seat; but accessible to the inventor's Rome Office was Odescalchi Palace in old, romantic nearby Civita Vecchia, on a small promontory jutting into the sea. When the home of the company in Alswyck, London, was moved to the Victoria Embankment, Marconi's office was located where he could "see the sun on the water . . . and hear the tooting of the tugboats."

In 1933 Mr. and Mrs. Marconi made a world tour which was a triumphal one for the father of wireless telegraphy. Now the question he was asked was: "Mr. Marconi, what do you think about television? How soon will we be able to see it?" He was apt to turn the answer away into a discussion of his latest microwave experimentations. "We have only touched the fringe of what electrical waves are capable of achieving," were his words.

- 23 -

LEE DE FOREST

1873 - 1961

FATHER OF THE RADIO INDUSTRY

DESCENDED from a French Huguenot family of long American residence, Lee de Forest was born at Council Bluffs, Iowa, August 26, 1873. The son of Reverend Henry Swift de Forest, a missionary, Lee knew straitened circumstances as the family moved from place to place in the Middle West and South.

An earnest, nervous, "ugly duckling" of a lad, young De Forest was torn by three different ambitions—to become a great musician, a great poet or a great inventor. At sixteen he made up his mind. "Dear Sir," he wrote his father, "will you favor me with your ear for a few moments? I intend to be an inventor, because I have great talents in that direction. . . . If this be so, why not allow me to so study as to best prepare myself for that profession? . . . Your obedient son, Lee de Forest."

Throughout his childhood the boy had shown many instances of inventive ability. That his determination to pursue this characteristic was wise is undeniable, for in the field of invention he won world fame as father of the radio industry.

At Yale, his father's alma mater, Lee entered the Sheffield Science School on a missionary scholarship. Quickly he became an intense student, so deeply absorbed in his subjects that he sometimes forgot to eat. Often, indeed, he had no money to buy food. Geometry he found easy. Physics was difficult, but so fascinating that he doggedly "determined to become proficient in it." When he published his autobiography in 1950, the inventor confessed that at college he had been "a 'greasy grind,' a creature held in general contempt by all normal Yale undergrads, myself among them."

On January 27, 1896, Lee's father died and left the family destitute. Tutoring and odd jobs enabled the young student to win his bachelor's degree and to go on with graduate work, completed in 1899. His doctoral thesis was "Reflection of Hertzian Waves from the Ends of Parallel Wires." The man voted the nerviest—and homeliest—in his class knew the road he would travel. "My one aim was to make my name at least rank with that of Marconi."

The little that was known of this newfangled thing, wireless, was due to Michael Faraday, James Clerk Maxwell and Heinrich Hertz who had suggested that ether waves traveled through space at a definite speed. In laboratory tests, Hertz had actually created and detected wireless waves. Then Guglielmo Marconi had demonstrated that "Hertzian waves" could carry messages if sparks were turned on and off according to a code. He had developed the magnetic detector—a tube of iron and nickel filings which "cohered" and conducted when radio, or ether, waves passed.

Here Lee de Forest entered the picture, earnestly striving to find better methods of detecting radio waves than with improvised "coherers" and detectors. He conducted his first experiments in the Western Electric Company's Chicago laboratory, later at the Armour Institute of Technology—now the Illinois Institute of Technology. Given the run of the institute's laboratory by Professor Clarence Freeman, the young inventor paid his way by helping students and caring for the apparatus. He lived on fifteen dollars a week earned in part-time editing of the *Western Electrician*. He brought the De Forest "responder" into being.

The United States Navy adopted De Forest's system and aided him in further development. He installed the navy's first five high-power radio stations, and frequently he set new records for long-distance wireless communication. Four years after graduating, the inventor realized his ambition to rank with Marconi!

At the height of his seeming success, De Forest was unexpectedly stripped of his patents and discharged from the company that had been created around him. Fortunately, however, his first backers allowed him to retain his worthless—in their opinion—pending patents.

While experimenting at the Armour Institute one evening six years earlier De Forest happened to be working by the light of an ordinary Welsbach gas burner. As he opened and closed his little spark transmitter, the light brightened and dimmed, an effect which the inventor was disappointed to find acoustical rather than electrical. Yet he became convinced that in gases enveloping an incandescent electrode resided "latent forces, or unrealized phenomena, which could be utilized in a detector of Hertzian oscillations [waves] far more delicate and sensitive than any known form of detecting device." In 1903 he had quietly rigged up a Bunsen burner so that the flame played on two platinum electrodes, one connected to an aerial wire and the other, through a telephone receiver, to the ground. With this device he picked up wireless signals from a ship in New York harbor.

Next he sought to heat incandescent gases directly by means of electric current. He had another bulb built that contained a carbon filament on one side and a platinum plate nearby. To increase the effect of the gas in the bulb, he wrapped a piece of tin foil around the outside. This third electrode was connected to the antenna and carried the incoming signal. By this time six years had elapsed since his first experiment in Chicago.

"I then realized that the efficiency could be still further enhanced if this third electrode were introduced *within* the [bulb]," De Forest later wrote. Next he discovered that placing this control electrode *between* the filament and the collecting plate increased its effectiveness. Finally, the third electrode functioned still better in the form of a grid, "a simple piece of wire bent back and forth located as close to the filament as possible."

"I recall as though it happened yesterday," he told a group of engineers meeting to honor him in 1920, "the thrill of significant achievement which possessed me on that sunny afternoon in early October 1906 as I hurried to my laboratory . . . to determine . . . whether my new 'grid audion' could bring in wireless signals over substantially greater distances than other receiving devices then in use. My eagerness grew with every step. To my excited delight I found it did; the faint impulses which my short antenna brought to that new grid electrode sounded many times louder in the headphones than any wireless signal ever heard before."

On October 25, 1906, De Forest applied for a patent on his tube, which he called an audion. This pending audion patent and its secret De Forest retained after losing his job and fortune in patents. Within months he formed a new company to launch his new invention, upon which, on January 15, 1907, he received famous Patent No. 841,387.

Nobel prize winner in physics Dr. I. I. Rabi has called the audion "so outstanding in its consequences that it almost ranks with the greatest inventions of all time." Though the electron was not generally accepted, the brilliant young experimenter strongly believed in the electronic theory of matter. In working to find a stronger signal, he had found not merely a magnifier of sounds, electrically translated. The audion magnified and translated into audible sensation *energies whose very exist-*

*ence as well as form and frequency might otherwise
have remained utterly unknown.*

Here, in essence, lay the greatness of De Forest's inventions. His audion opened the door to the field of electronics.

Initially developed as a detector, the audion, as an
amplifier, made possible long-distance telephoning. The
first epochal coast-to-coast telephone conversation in
1915 owed its success to De Forest's invention. Then the
audion became the prototype of the billions of radio
tubes that have been sold since. Thus all modern radio
and television was made possible by De Forest's triode
tube.

Temperamental, restless and, above all, independent,
De Forest made and lost three fortunes. Constantly har-
assed by financial and patent difficulties, he nevertheless
never forsook his beloved research. Always he ven-
tured into realms unknown. After selling his audion
rights to Western Electric, he turned to the synchroni-
zation of sound and movement. In the early 1920s his
phonofilm helped usher in the modern talking motion
picture. A decade later his talents and energies were
probing the still unopened area of television. Obtaining
over three hundred patents between 1930 to 1950, De
Forest contributed so importantly to the new field that
he is sometimes known as the grandfather of television.

Universally recognized as the father of radio, Lee de
Forest little dreamed, when he invented the grid-con-
trolled tube, its profound technical and social consequences. How would anyone, even an elated inventor,

conceive that radio would bring forth the second revolution in communication—one far greater than that resulting from the introduction of the telegraph and telephone? For radio and television constitute the greatest mass communications media in history. So swift is the radio that a speaker's voice speeds to millions of listeners the nation over before it reaches the back row of an auditorium from which an address is broadcast. Traveling with the speed of light and requiring no wires or cables, radio communication can even circle the globe before sound waves travel from a speaker's rostrum to his physically present audience.

By 1925 radio was carrying the news of the world, entertainment and helpful information into 2,000,000 American homes. Fourteen years later the new industry was producing over 10,000,000 radio sets annually. Today, ninety-five per cent of our nation's homes enjoy at least one radio set, and television approaches that figure as it rapidly spreads into new areas.

Moreover, the full story of the magical tube that De Forest tested in his attic laboratory in New York that August day of 1906 must include the myriad developments in electronics. Radar, an offshoot, not only revolutionized modern warfare but stands today in the front line of our air defense, as well as piloting and landing planes. Modern electronic industrial devices control motors and other machines or aid manufacturing processes by sorting, testing, measuring and counting products of all sorts. Other such applications help prevent accidents or cleverly solve intricate mathematical problems for engineers and scientists. Electronic instruments helped to introduce automation into certain manufacturing operations and brought great advances to the science and art of healing. Without electronics, nuclear research could not exist. And riding in the warheads of giant rockets are electronic devices which may point the way to a new era in communications or even to interplanetary travel. Such are the developments to which De Forest furnished an invaluable key.

So abundant was De Forest's energy that, late in life and in comfortable circumstances, he took up mountaineering as a hobby. On his seventieth birthday he climbed Mount Whitney, the highest peak in the United States.

Before his death on June 30, 1961 De Forest indulged in reminiscing. Disappointment and agony of invention, problems of litigation and finance had only mellowed him. "Looking back," he wrote, "I realize that these difficulties are what made my life interesting to me."

Was De Forest a born inventor, a natural genius? If such characteristics exist in people, certainly he had them in full measure. Nevertheless, in his boyhood letter to his father, he realized need for a scientific education to bring fulfillment to his natural talent for invention. In graduate school the lectures of Dr. Josiah Willard Gibbs—sometimes known as the American Isaac Newton—entranced the earnest young scientist. "I can fervently say," he later wrote, "that it was Williard Gibbs' influence and inspiration which so firmly resolved me . . . to prepare myself for that project in research and invention which I had determined should be my life's work." Once embarked on his chosen profession, he relentlessly pursued it. The result was achievement and happiness.

In revealing his own struggles, disappointments and successes in his autobiography, De Forest hoped "to encourage others to embark on a similar career of discovery and invention." Strongly he believed that "opportunities today are just as great as they were at the start of the century."

- 24 -

CHARLES MARTIN HALL

1863 - 1914

FATHER OF THE ALUMINUM INDUSTRY

IN CHARLES MARTIN HALL'S CHEMISTRY CLASS at Oberlin College one day in the 1880s Professor Frank Jewett lectured on a curious metal called aluminum. Though little known, it was not new. Hans Christian Oersted, a Danish scientist, had, in 1825, first isolated small beads of the metal and identified it as a new and unusual element. Aluminum-bearing clays were known to be practically everywhere. But so securely was the metal locked in its oxide form that only costly and intricate chemical processes could free it from its ore. Yet aluminum was light and ductile. It was a good conductor of electricity and resistant to corrosion. Its silvery color had artistic appeal.

Indeed, if its production cost could be substantially reduced, the metal might well have a brilliant future.

The "if" loomed large. Following Oersted, other scientists had produced the metal in quantity, but at prohibitive cost. Its price of fifteen dollars a pound in 1885 made it almost a precious metal.

Young Charles Martin Hall listened intently as Professor Jewett ended his lecture, "If anyone should invent a process by which aluminum could be made cheaply on a commercial scale, not only would he be a benefactor to the world, but [he] would also be able to lay up for himself a great fortune!"

To a classmate Charles whispered, "I'll be that man!"

Charles Martin Hall was born at Thompson, Ohio, December 6, 1863. He had moved to the college town of Oberlin in that state when a boy. His father, Reverend Hemen Bassett Hall, had a pastorate there. Both his father and mother, Sophronia Brooks Hall, were Oberlin graduates. The family home was not far from the college campus.

Since his boyhood Charles had loved scientific books and experiments. One of his early chemical experiments had momentarily endangered the Hall home, though it had resulted only in a burned tablecloth and a stern parental lecture. At college he had been an avid student, and now the challenge of Professor Jewett's lecture gave direction and purpose to his studies. The teacher encouraged his pupil's dedication to his self-imposed task.

In his father's woodshed the young scientist fitted out a makeshift laboratory. There he went to work, constantly assisted by Julia, his next oldest sister, a former chemistry student at Oberlin. First attempting to isolate

Statue of young Hall in Oberlin College

aluminum by chemical reaction, Charles failed so completely and so often that he ruled out that means of attack. Perhaps, he reasoned, the answer might lie in electrolysis, a method of separating some chemical compounds by dissolving them in a suitable electrolyte and passing an electric current through the solution.

Finding a waterless liquid that would dissolve aluminum oxide, or alumina, as it was also known, was Charles's first problem. In June 1885, when he was graduated from Oberlin, he was still seeking the answer.

By February 1886, however, only two months after celebrating his twenty-second birthday, Charles had discovered that the mineral cryolite in its molten form would effectively dissolve alumina. Excitedly he prepared for the real test.

On February 16 he was ready. With Julia's help, he attached wires from a crude battery to a clay crucible holding the cryolite-alumina mixture. He threw the switch to start the current. Brother and sister watched breathlessly. Minutes dragged. Then Charles opened the crucible. That some decomposition was occurring was evident from the reaction, but no silvery aluminum gleamed in the molten mixture. Perhaps the fault was in the clay crucible.

Charles decided to fashion a small crucible of carbon. On February 23, only seven days after the first test, he tried again. This time he fed current through the red-hot molten solution for several hours. After allowing the mixture to cool, he broke up the solid mass. Scarcely could he and Julia force themselves to look. Then their eyes beheld shining lumps of aluminum.

Charles whooped, snatched up the silvery globules and rushed to show them to Professor Jewett. The teacher knew that the years-long search had ended. The youth standing before him had won where eminent scientists had failed or only partially succeeded. The good professor never himself claimed any credit, except to declare, "My great discovery has been the discovery of a man—Charles Martin Hall."

With aluminum abundant—geologists have estimated that it constitutes eight per cent of the earth's crust—and with a promising method of producing it cheaply, Charles seemed certain of great financial success.

He met with shock and disappointment. In July 1886 the young inventor filed his patent application, only to have the Patent Office reply that Paul L. T. Heroult, a Frenchman who, incidentally, was the same age as Hall, had already filed a similar claim. Two years later, however, Charles received a pioneer patent which he later sustained against infringers. He proved beyond question that he had reduced his invention to practice on February 23, 1886, while the French youth had to rely on April 23, 1886, the date he had filed his application in France.

His patent secured, young Hall faced the task of finding men with money to invest and an interest in new ideas. But his enthusiasm was not contagious. That he held the key to commercial production of an intriguing metal businessmen would grant, but to what uses could this untried aluminum be put compared with those of

iron, steel, copper, lead or zinc? If only he could find
someone to believe in aluminum's potentialities!

His determination was rewarded in 1888 with the
formation, through Captain Alfred E. Hunt and several
Pittsburgh associates, of the Pittsburgh Reduction Company, later to become Aluminum Company of America.
Hall, Captain Hunt and a group of farsighted Pittsburgh
businessmen were the first stockholders. Within a few
months a pilot plant was operating. Thanksgiving Day,
1888, saw the first aluminum ingot poured.

Hall's assistant at the plant on Smallman Street was
Arthur V. Davis, a young Amherst graduate who later
became the company's president and chairman of the
board of directors. Tirelessly "spelling" each other in
twelve-hour shifts, they soon had a hundred pounds of
aluminum stored in the office safe. Yet many early manufacturing problems required patient experimentation.
Realization of his dream of wealth still eluded Hall. He
lived frugally in a boardinghouse near the plant.

In financing its expanding activities, however, the
Pittsburgh Reduction Company managed to secure additional capital for several years. Finally its prospects
seemed so promising that Pittsburgh businessmen An-
drew W. and Richard M. Mellon personally invested
in the firm. This was the boost the company needed—
now improvements could be made and production increased.

Yet the aluminum industry still had a rocky road to
travel. To absorb increasing production, new markets
had to be found. To give the metal greater strength and

broaden its range of applications, alloys had to be developed. For decorative purposes and to provide additional protection under adverse conditions, finishes had to be found. And, to fit the useful metal to hundreds of new applications, methods of joining—of riveting, welding and brazing—had to be developed. Gradually these goals were attained.

Today the primary products of aluminum are fabricated by almost every metalworking process. It is cast into ingots. It is rolled into plate, sheet and foil, and into structural shapes, such as rod and bar. It is drawn into wire and stranded into cable for electrical transmission lines, and extruded into thousands of useful and ornamental forms. Forgings, castings and paint pigments also are made of aluminum.

Great vision was necessary to see these vast potentialities in aluminum. Incident to each new use new problems arose. A vigorous sales force worked at convincing skeptics. Salesmen taught customers how to use the new metal. Only the faith of stockholders and the perseverance of men like Hall, Hunt and Davis pulled the industry through its precarious early years.

In 1890 aluminum made its bow to the public in the humble form of pots and pans. Who would have guessed, at the time, that the pioneering efforts of these men would help the aviation industry to fill the skies with aircraft clad in gleaming aluminum?

Yet the youthful metal figured importantly in the development of many industries. Alert automotive manufacturers used great quantities of aluminum in body and engine parts. Numerous early uses of the metal in railroad cars foretold the low-slung aluminum streamliners which now streak across continents. So completely did aluminum figure in the expansion of America that, in 1939, *Life* magazine hailed it as, "by all odds, the theme metal of the 20th Century." Today, sturdy lightweight aluminum has over four thousand different applications.

Throughout his life Hall possessed a great desire to learn. Dedicated to science as he was, he made his technical education pay him well. Yet his interests were many and varied. He was at home in art and literature. He collected fine rugs. He was a sensitive pianist. In his many travels he sought out-of-the-way places which poets and writers had enshrined.

Never a man of robust health, in his last years Hall fought valiantly to regain his strength and return to research. But, on December 27, 1914, at the age of fifty-one, he died in Daytona, Florida.

Hall profited by his discovery far beyond his wildest dream. For years he was vice-president of Aluminum Company of America. Though spending relatively little on himself and never marrying, he gave generously to educational and charitable institutions in many lands. To his beloved alma mater he left a substantial part of his $30,000,000 fortune.

In 1953, when the Sophronia Brooks Hall Auditorium, honoring Charles's mother, was dedicated at Oberlin College, an observer recalled Hall's graduation oration of 1885. Speaking on "Science and Imagination," uncannily young Hall had analyzed his future career which truly blended science and imagination.

Thus Charles Martin Hall left a legacy not merely of a new industry but of challenge to the youth of today. With education and with imagination, the rewards in satisfaction and security in the vastly multiplied opportunities of modern science and engineering are theirs for the asking. And they, too, can play a part in producing the benefactions of science.

Professor Jewett's prediction became a reality. Charles Martin Hall did become a benefactor to the world and also acquired for himself a great fortune.

WILLIS HAVILAND CARRIER

1876 - 1950

FATHER OF THE AIR CONDITIONING INDUSTRY

ASTONISHING ACCOMPLISHMENT abounds in the story of the air conditioning industry. Most surprising of all, perhaps, is the fact that the industry survived the many complications of its early years. And, without the dedicated genius of Willis Haviland Carrier, it might well have died in infancy.

Carrier was born on November 26, 1876, of "rugged and adventurous" British descent, on a farm which his great-grandfather had slashed from the forest near Angola in western New York. The boy's father, Duane Carrier, held to farming. Young Willis, however, soon showed inventive and mechanical skills, inherited, perhaps, from his mother. For Elizabeth Haviland Carrier, rather than her farmer husband, fixed the family clocks and repaired the sewing machine. More important, she taught Willis fractions and other simple mathematics with a stimulating simplicity. Years later he was to say that she opened "a new world to me and gave me a pattern for solving problems that I've followed ever since."

Willis lost his mother when he was only eleven, but her traits were strong in him. Already he was working on a "perpetual motion machine." After chores and homework he habitually burned the midnight oil while solving self-invented problems. Later a friend recalled once finding him working geometry problems outdoors, utterly unmindful of falling snow. Long before his graduation from Angola High, the farm boy was obsessed with the ambition of going to Cornell and becoming an engineer.

When Willis was fifteen his father married Eugenia Tifft Martin, a widow with three grown children. To the home of one of them, a Buffalo veterinarian, the boy was sent to earn his keep and to partake of Central High's better curriculum as a means of furthering his ambition. By dint of winning a state scholarship and by "stretching his funds" and taking odd jobs of all types, Willis left Cornell in June 1901 with a mechanical engineer's degree in electrical engineering. In the same class was Claire Seymour, whom he married a year later.

Shortly after Carrier's graduation he experienced a chance meeting which proved fortunate for himself and the industry he was to found. On a Buffalo streetcar he asked a young stranger for directions to the Buffalo Forge Company, where he expected to apply for a position. The stranger, Irvine Lyle, two years older than

Carrier, was a salesman for the company. The instant friendship which they felt grew into a lifelong business association. Lyle complemented Carrier's engineering wizardry with talented sales and business abilities. He brought challenge and soundness to pioneering industrial effort.

The Buffalo Forge Company made blowers, exhausters and heaters. Almost before Carrier had settled in his first job he found himself not only a "heating engineer" but also the head of a new experimental department. And Lyle, himself an engineer, was turning over to Carrier the difficult problems of his customers. An early one involved a printing plant's concern with humidity control, a problem that had long defied scientists and inventors.

By the turn of the nineteenth century it was apparent that new industrial techniques and precision equipment required more thorough control of indoor climate. And progress was being made in many of the areas now allied with true air conditioning. Advances in mechanical refrigeration devices, heating, cooling, and ventilation fans, steam condensers, humidifiers, purifiers, heaters and washers were providing manufacturing operations with important, though incomplete, elements of climate control.

In many of these industries, however, continued progress was threatened by problems of uncontrolled temperature and humidity which affected not only production and products but also worker comfort and efficiency. In short, the knowledge and practice of what we know today as air conditioning were, in Carrier's early manhood, a chaotic jumble.

Though man had learned how to cool and circulate air, he knew little or nothing about controlling its absolute and relative humidity—a primary element in effective air conditioning. In the first major job Lyle gave him, the twenty-five-year-old Carrier reduced the problem to simple terms with his orderly and trained mind. A Brooklyn printing plant was having production difficulties because changing amounts of moisture caused the paper to expand or contract during the printing. Carrier found out the proper degree of moisture needed in the air for printing processes. He then went to Weather Bureau tables which showed him the precise temperature the air should be in order to hold that much moisture. Then he set about designing air cooling equipment that would produce that temperature and the proper rates of air flow to maintain it. As a result of these computations he was able to specify the temperature of the cooling water that flows through refrigeration coils and the size and number of coils needed.

Because of Carrier's pioneer use of humidity control, authorities recognize this 1902 installation as marking the birth of the modern air conditioning industry, *a substantial accomplishment for an engineer one year out of college.*

Carrier quickly supplemented this development with the invention of an apparatus to produce fog mechanically. Later he recalled his conception of the idea. Standing on a Pittsburgh railway platform, he had been contemplating that city's then famous smog. The temperature was in the low thirties. "Here," he theorized, "is air approximately one hundred per cent saturated with moisture. The temperature is low, so, even though saturated, there is not much actual moisture. . . . Now, if I can saturate air and control its temperature at saturation, I can get air with any amount of moisture in it I want. I can do it, too, by drawing air through a fine spray of water to create actual fog. By controlling the water temperature I can control the temperature at saturation. When very moist air is desired, I'll heat the water. When very dry air is desired, I'll use cold water to get low temperature saturation. The cold water spray will actually be the condensing surface."

Adapting a nozzle originally designed for an insecticide spray, he patented his "Apparatus for Treating Air" on January 2, 1906. Eventually this development resulted in dew-point control, "the fundamental basis of the entire air conditioning industry."

During 1906 Carrier and Stuart W. Cramer of Charlotte, North Carolina, independently developed different systems of automatic humidity control for cotton mills, which need moist air for efficient production. The two men made possible the modern textile industry. In describing his process Cramer first used the term "air conditioning" and thus named an industry. At Lyle's behest the pleased William F. Wendt, president of the Buffalo Forge Company, named a subsidiary the "Carrier Air Conditioning Company of America" in honor of his young research and engineering head.

Though happy with his own progress, Carrier was concerned with the state of the new industry. He questioned the accuracy of the generally accepted psychrometric data, or measurements of temperature and humidity, upon which the industry relied. In 1911 he presented a paper titled "Rational Psychrometric Formulae," giving authoritative bases for all fundamental calculations. The principles—which he had reasoned out theoretically and then proved experimentally—gave the air conditioning industry a firm foundation and impetus for advancement.

By 1914 Carrier had designed and installed air conditioning systems for printing, paper and textile plants; for malt houses, department stores, hotels and pharmaceutical plants; for soap, rubber and tobacco factories; for candy and processed food plants; and for film studios, breweries, bakeries and meat-packing houses. Meanwhile, within the company, Carrier, Lyle and five other young and enthusiastic engineers had come to constitute an informal group known as "The Seven." They were prominent in the firm and in their profession. Yet trouble loomed ahead.

The outbreak of World War I brought to the Buffalo Forge Company a pressing need for retrenchment. The decision was made to drop the intricate and specialized air conditioning division. While Carrier and Lyle would be retained, most of the other members of "The Seven" would go.

But Carrier and Lyle joined with the five other young engineers and staked their savings—a total of only

$32,600—and their futures on the Carrier Engineering Corporation—later Carrier Corporation—which they incorporated in 1915. Carrier was president and Lyle treasurer and general manager. It was a daring venture, for the industry was still in its infancy and its future uncertain, even precarious. Yet it was expressive of Carrier's complete self-confidence and of the others' full trust in him. To them he was simply "The Chief," in part a tribute to his leadership, in part an expression of deep affection.

Carrier's early accomplishments in air conditioning amounted to real engineering feats. Each installation was virtually a separate problem, involving specialized applications of thermodynamics and psychrometry, themselves sciences still in the process of development. Each installation depended upon equipment and materials, some available and others that had to be designed for air conditioning use. Immediately Carrier and Lyle undertook pioneering work in standardizing equipment, methods and practices.

Most installations thus far had been to condition air for products and processes. Nearly a decade elapsed before improvements and refinements made by Carrier and Lyle were to point the way to a goal they had long envisioned—air conditioning for the health and comfort of humans.

In attaining that goal "The Chief" assumed loads far heavier than he had carried before. Each challenging job he made into a triumph, and a new day unfolded for air conditioning. A random sampling of installations by the company which Carrier founded includes Madison Square Garden, New York City; the House and Senate Chambers and the Pentagon, Washington; the United Nations Secretariat, New York City; the Merchandise Mart, Chicago; Gateway Center, Pittsburgh; the Railway Exchange Building, St. Louis; Lever House, New York City; the Republic National Bank, Dallas; the newest U.S. atomic submarines; the Cleveland Municipal Auditorium; and the New York International Airport at Idlewild.

It was Carrier's destiny to contribute to and live through the full cycle of the industry he founded. He was as much a factor in the building of small conditioning units for stores, homes and single rooms, and in developing a winter air conditioner with provision for summer cooling, as he was in the epochal large installations previously listed.

Carrier's associates, of course, contributed materially to these accomplishments, and one of them remembered that, "incredible as it may seem, 'The Chief' was never 'too busy.' He always 'had time.' He was constantly interested in developing young people. Great as were his scientific achievements—and they were great indeed—Dr. Carrier's supreme ability was to teach and inspire."

In the inventor's own mind his greatest engineering achievement was the designing of a vital air conditioning and refrigeration system for a wind tunnel in which the U.S. Air Force simulated high-altitude conditions to test prototype planes. He tackled the job during 1942, in his sixty-fifth year. Experiments made in the Wright

Field wind tunnel were credited with having shortened World War II by many months.

Carrier married three times. A year after the death of his first wife in 1912, he wed Jennie Martin, who died in 1939. In 1941 he married Elizabeth Marsh Wise, with whom he made a triumphal tour of South America. As the engineer who had brought air conditioning to many of the world's countries, Carrier traveled extensively and received many honors from colleges and scientific societies.

Following a heart attack in 1947, Carrier courageously obeyed strict doctor's orders for three years. Twenty hours of every day he spent lying in a horizontal position. Yet with a pad of paper on his knees and his slide rule close at hand, he strove to simplify complex calculations or to express vague concepts in concrete terms. Often, however, he visited his office. On October 9, 1950, shortly before his seventy-fourth birthday, he died in New York City.

Many of his dreams—often deemed fantastic when he first revealed them—had been fulfilled. His concept that indoor climate could be controlled has changed our life. It is still changing it as large air conditioning installations and small air conditioning units available in "packages" provide year-round human comfort in factories and hospitals, in offices and homes. Furthermore, accurate control of humidity plays an increasingly important role in more than two hundred industries, helping make countless products better, cheaper and faster. Who can tell but that his prophecy of entire cities air conditioned from a central plant may not come true?

That air conditioning, born for special industrial purposes, should have burst into incredible and universal usefulness is in itself a miracle story. That one man should have been responsible for so much of it is amazing—a working genius of an engineer who first learned from his mother how to order his mind and his life.